PILO

By
JASON HALES

Inspired by true events

Dedicated to my son, Matthew, a true warrior
and to all the other kids still in the fight.

ISBN: 978-1-64945-701-1 (Paperback)

Library of Congress Control Number: 2020911452

Book Cover Design by ebooklaunch.com

Printed in the United States of America.

First printing edition 2020.

Targhee Press
4544 Stonebrook Ln
Idaho Falls, ID 83404
www.targheepress.com

PROLOGUE

SPARTAN KIDS WORLD CHAMPIONSHIP LAUGHLIN, NEVADA

The low wall I stood behind held back the electric energy of the group of boys I found myself with that dusty, crisp morning in the desert. The youngest was ten years old, but the older ones were thirteen, like me. We all gathered on this rocky foothill outside Laughlin, Nevada to compete in the Spartan Kids World Championship Race. During a Spartan Race, the adult runners plunge into mud, climb ropes or cargo nets, carry sandbags, or swing across monkey bars. For kids, we do a lot of the same obstacles but with lighter sandbags and shorter climbs. We also run between one to two miles. But not in this race. The championship race was three miles long, with about forty obstacles. Luckily, it was November, and the weather was not too hot.

On my left, I saw a kid who just finished speaking with his private coach. Who hires a private coach for an event like this? The boys in front of me chatted excitedly in Spanish, and I had no idea what they were saying. Another boy nearby traveled here from Japan, and he looked as nervous as I felt. In all, ten different countries were represented among the fifty boys in my group. I looked at the racing sleeves they gave me, tight spandex sleeves meant to protect me from the grit and gravel of the race. The sleeves were also colored with red and white stripes, with patches of dark blue and white stars. I was representing the United States, which was really cool.

To race in the championship, we all had to finish in first, second, or third place at one of the regional races held around the world. I ran in the Spartan Kids Race in Eden, Utah, earlier in the year during the summer. Among the more than sixty boys in that race, I managed to finish third, which qualified me to attend this championship. All of us here at the Spartan Kids World Championship earned our spot behind the wall. All of us want to win. All of us sacrificed to get here. But I am not like the other boys. I survived a brain tumor, a big one. The story of how I ended up behind this wall began almost five years ago.

Chapter 1

Five Years Earlier

"Aaaaahhhh!" I screamed in pain as I closed my eyes and held my head on our family room couch. I was trying to watch TV but my head felt like it was being run over by a school bus.

"Matt, what is the matter?" my mom asked while standing in the kitchen, putting some lunch together for my three-year-old brother, Owen. Owen is the youngest of all of us kids, and he gets whatever he wants. I'm child number two, which means all I get is tough love.

"My head hurts!" I shouted, not understanding why my mom didn't get it. During our conversation, my dad walked inside the house after mowing the lawn. It was October, and he was hoping to be done mowing for the next six months.

"What's the matter, bud?" my dad asked me.

"My head," I moaned. He looked at my mom then walked over to her. I covered my head with a blanket and tried to block out the afternoon sunlight pouring in through our sliding glass door. I heard them whisper back and forth. I couldn't hear all the words they said, but I heard my mom say something about going to a doctor, followed by my dad saying the word *dramatic*. I know what dramatic means, and I was not being dramatic. My head hurt like crazy. I heard a cabinet open, the scraping sound of a childproof lid on a medicine bottle being opened, followed by the sound of a glass filling with water and then, footsteps from my dad as he walked over to me.

"Here, take some medicine to help your headache. If it still hurts in a little while, we'll take you in to see the doctor," he said reassuringly.

I took the small cup of liquid pain reliever and swallowed it, followed by a few big gulps of some cool water. I laid down and covered my head again, no longer interested in the TV. I napped for a little while, but woke up with a headache still, just not as bad. I reached for my glasses and put them on. I wanted to go outside for a little while. Winter comes fast in Idaho, and I wanted to enjoy the warm sun on this Saturday before it was gone.

"Hey, Matt, how's your head feeling?" my dad called to me as I got up.

"Fine," I lied as I walked out into the sunlight, closing the door to the garage behind me. No way was I going to spend my Saturday visiting with a doctor.

Weeks passed, and fall leaves were quickly replaced by snowdrifts. My headaches continued, though not as bad as that Saturday in October. My mom always asked about the headaches, wanting to know if they were getting worse or better. My mom doesn't like seeing us in pain. Like the time my younger sister, Rachel, decided to make her own smoothie using an immersion blender. She was six at the time, and after blending a few ingredients, she decided to clean the blade without unplugging the blender. Well, she accidentally hit the power button while her finger was on the blade. She screamed as blood spattered everywhere! I called for my mom, who came down the stairs in a flash.

"Jason!" she yelled when she saw Rachel's bloody hand. Moments later, my dad came running up from his basement office to see what was going on. He saw the blood and immediately grabbed some paper towels to wrap around

Rachel's finger and apply pressure. He held it there for a few seconds, then removed it to see the damage. My dad was an EMT in college, which means he knows a few things about first aid even though he now works for a publishing company.

"Yeah, she's going to need stitches," he said, looking at my mom. "Do you want me to take her?"

"No, I'll take her," said my mom. She ran out to the garage to start the minivan.

"OK. Rachel," said my dad looking down at her tiny body, "Mom's going to take you to the doctor. You need to get some stitches."

Rachel looked horrified and started to whimper. Then she did something really weird. Her eyes rolled into the back of her head, and she went boneless, which is what us kids say when someone goes completely limp everywhere, usually on purpose. Dad had to pick up her whole body to keep her from hitting the ground.

"Rach," said my dad, lightly tapping on her cheek. "Rach!" he yelled a little louder.

"What's going on?" my mom said in alarm as she came in from the garage and heard my dad yelling.

"She fainted," said my dad evenly. He doesn't really get too worked up about anything, unless he's fishing and the fish he is reeling in gets off the hook. I don't understand all the words he says at those times, but I can tell he is not happy when that happens.

Rachel's head began to rise as she regained consciousness. Dad carried her out to the minivan with my mom following closely behind. Moments later, he walked back inside and headed straight to the front window of our house to watch my mom and Rachel leave.

"Will Rachel be OK?" I asked.

"Yeah, she'll be fine. She just needs a few stitches. She was glad Mom was taking her."

"What happened?" asked my older brother, Will. He is two years older than me and missed out on all the action. He had been building something cool with Legos in his room upstairs, probably a spaceship.

"Rachel has to get stitches," I said. Will looked at my dad for an explanation as he walked into the kitchen.

"Rachel decided to make her own smoothie," said my dad, grabbing the blender and heading towards the sink. "And apparently she managed to turn her finger into hamburger."

"Eew," said Will, making a face.

Rachel came home a few hours later with some stitches in her finger. A week later, my dad cut the stitches out and her finger looked normal, though she said her finger felt strange and tingly. During those days, as Rachel recovered, my mom always checked on her. My mom is pretty good at making us kids feel better.

CHAPTER 2

December means two things: my birthday and Christmas. We celebrated my ninth birthday with tacos and cake, two of my favorite foods. A few days later, school ended, and I got to enjoy the Christmas break. For the most part, the break went OK. I did have a few headaches, but since they weren't too severe, my mom and dad assumed it was a cold or flu bug since everyone was getting it. In January, I was excited to get back to school. I was a third-grader in a multi-grade class, which meant we had first, second- and third-graders all mixed together. My teacher, Mrs. Ball, was awesome and had all of us third graders mentor the younger kids. My sister, Rachel, was one of the first-graders. It was not always easy having my sister in my class.

After a few weeks of school passed by, something weird happened to me. I was sitting in class, and then all of a sudden, my stomach felt sick. I ran over to Mrs. Ball.

"Mrs. Ball? I don't feel very good," I said, holding my stomach.

"Do you think you might throw up?" she asked.

I nodded.

"Then try to get to the bathroom!" she said with some urgency in her voice.

Eventually, I walked back into the class and felt better, but I had just puked my entire breakfast into the toilet. Mrs. Ball saw me enter through the door and walked over to me, leaving the group of kids she was working with in a confused huddle.

"How are you feeling, Matt? You look pale."

"I feel better now," I replied, seeing the worry on her face.

"Did you throw up?"

"Yeah."

"Well, head down to the nurse's office, and have her call your mom," she said, patting me on the shoulder.

I hate sitting in the nurse's office. After the nurse took my temperature and told me I was "cool as a cucumber"—side note, cucumbers are not cool—she called my mom and told me to wait outside by the receptionist. The ladies in the office were chatting quietly, sometimes looking over at me. I just slumped on the bench and jammed my hands into my coat pockets. After what seemed like forever, my mom showed up with my little brother Owen.

"Hi, Jen," said the receptionist.

"Hi," my mom smiled back as she began signing something on a clipboard.

"How are you feeling?" Mom asked me as I stood up and walked over to her.

"OK, I guess," I said, frowning a little. Mom looked at me with that look moms have when they feel sorry for their kids. She finished signing me out and thanked the receptionist.

"Feel better, Matt," the receptionist called after me as we left the office. I just wanted to get home.

The brisk January air hit us right in the face as we stepped outside. I heard Mom catch her breath as she tried to avoid the arctic blast. Man, Idaho can get really cold! Owen watched as his breath turned into puffy clouds.

"Mommy, I'm a choo choo!" he squealed.

Mom and I both laughed at Owen. He always tries to make people laugh. Mom placed her icy hand on my forehead as we arrived at the minivan.

"Ugh, your hand is cold!" I said.

"You feel a little warm," she said, ignoring my comment as she removed her hand and started up the minivan's engine.

"That's only because your hand is freezing. The nurse said I was fine. Do I have to go to the doctor?" I asked, hoping I didn't have to go. What if they poke me with a needle?

"Not yet. We'll see how you are doing in the morning."

CHAPTER 3

The next morning my mom said I had a fever, which sucked because that meant I had to go see a doctor. My dad was out of town for work, and I could hear my mom talking to him on the phone.

"Yeah, he still has a fever . . . He said he has a little headache, but that it's not too bad . . . I'm telling you, I think something is really wrong here, this isn't like him . . . OK, I'll let you know . . . Love you too . . . OK, travel safe . . . Bye."

After Will and Rachel left for school, my mom called the doctor's office and made an appointment for later in the morning.

"Matt, I'm going to go shower and get ready. Can you keep an eye on Owen for me?"

I nodded, "Sure."

I looked over at Owen as my mom went upstairs. He was watching a cartoon on the TV and patting his belly as it stuck out of his pajamas. Owen only cared about food, the TV, and making funny noises with his body. I sometimes wondered if he ever thought about anything else.

I laid down on the couch, and dozed off while my mom got ready. Time passed quickly while I slept and before I knew it, we were headed to see the doctor.

After a bunch of pinching and poking, the doctor left to do whatever doctors do after they ask all their questions. I stared at the painted walls. Each room in the office had a different theme. This one was kind of cool. It was painted to look like a lake in the mountains with various people riding horses, fishing, and boating.

"What are you thinking about, Matt?" Mom asked. But before I could answer, there was a knock at the door, and the doctor walked back in and sat down in front of me.

"Well, Matt," he began, "it looks like you have hand, foot, and mouth disease. Since you have been running a fever and have a little bit of red spotting in your mouth, I think we may have caught it early. It can explain why you have had some headaches and why you threw up. Those aren't the most common symptoms, but they do happen sometimes."

My mom didn't look convinced.

"So how do we treat it?" she asked.

"You can just use children's Tylenol or ibuprofen. If Matt needs something stronger, just call the office, and I can prescribe something." He closed his laptop, gave a brief smile, and then walked out through the door.

CHAPTER 4

My headaches kept coming back. Sometimes they were really bad, like I wanted to scream my head off kind of bad, and other times they were a constant ache which would never leave. Every once in a while, my stomach felt weird and my eyes hurt. I figured if I took off my glasses, my eyes would stop hurting, but they never did. So I dealt with it. I didn't want to tell my mom about the headaches or eye pain because I knew she would take me to the doctor again, and I didn't want to have that ruining day. I'm glad my mom takes such good care of us kids, but I just hate seeing the doctor, especially when they need to give me shots. Those are the worst!

It was almost May now, and the snow was all gone. We were allowed to play out on the playground more often, at least when it was not raining. I usually left my glasses on my desk when we went outside, but I forgot to do that.

"Hey, Matt, let's play tag with the other kids," my friend Kotter said, pulling me by the arm. I've known Kotter ever since we were about three years old. He has sandy hair and likes to spike it up everywhere.

"Just a second," I said, taking my glasses off. "I forgot to leave my glasses on my desk. I need to run back inside and leave them there."

"No, that will take too long," Kotter plead. "Just put them in your pocket."

I thought that sounded like a good idea, so I shoved them in my pocket and ran with Kotter to the group playing tag.

"Who's 'it'?" asked Kotter.

"Take a knee!" shouted a tall boy in the group. Everyone dropped to a knee. Unofficial playground rules said that whoever was the last one to kneel would be 'it'. In this case, it was Tom.

Tom lives for playing tag, in fact, it is all he talks about in class. Compared to the rest of us third graders, Tom was huge and was fast. He relished being 'it' while playing tag. In fact, he never tagged anyone. He shoved them. Hard. And for some reason, he always found it funny. It's not that he was mean by nature. He just believed that all sports were full-contact sports.

"Better run!" he grinned, popping his knuckles and cracking his neck.

Like sheep before a wolf, we scattered across the open field, screaming and yelling playfully. The warm sun felt great and the fresh air smelled like flowers. Kotter and I ran towards the playground equipment. Usually, kids agreed that you couldn't climb on the equipment. However, you could run around the swings, slides, and monkey bars to avoid being tagged. Tom's barrel-shaped body darted among the kids, his mop of black hair swinging across his face, obscuring the glint of excitement in his eyes.

"Oh no," Kotter moaned. I turned and looked where Kotter was pointing. Calvin, a small boy in our class, was kneeling down and tying his shoes. He never saw the freight train called Tom coming.

Tom reminded me of The Hulk, who only wanted to smash. He desperately wanted to grow up to be a linebacker just for the pleasure of sacking an unsuspecting quarterback. Unfortunately, Calvin was his unsuspecting quarterback. Tom ran at Calvin with the energy of a runaway semi heading down a mountain with no brakes. One moment Calvin was finishing up a granny knot, and the next he was covered in grass and most likely got a bruise somewhere along his ribcage.

"Calvin's 'it'!" Tom bellowed as Calvin slowly pieced together what had just happened.

Calvin was a quiet kid. Though he never said much, everyone really liked him. Another boy, Kaden, walked over to Calvin. Kaden had a reputation for being fast. Like, cheetah fast.

When Kaden reached Calvin, he extended his hand to help him up.

"If I touch you, you're 'it'," Calvin said, looking at Kaden hopefully.

"I know. I'm counting on it."

Calvin accepted the extended hand and rose up.

"Kaden's 'it'!" Calvin yelled. The two smiled at each other as Kaden ran off.

"This is going to be good," Kotter chortled.

"Yeah!" I agreed. We ran over to the spiral slide to get a better view.

Kids scattered before Kaden, but he paid no attention to them. His eyes were fixed on Tom. Over the last year, Kaden has grown taller and faster. It took Tom a moment to process what was happening. Then, he did something unexpected. Tom ran, or at least tried to.

"I think Kaden is going to plow into Tom," I said in disbelief.

"I think you're right," agreed Kotter. "This is epic!"

Tom bobbed and weaved, but it proved to be futile. In seconds, Kaden was on Tom like a cheetah chasing down a gazelle. Tom had no chance. With a final surge of energy, Kaden shoved both palms into Tom's shoulder blades with such force it sent Tom face-first into the grass. Tom rolled twice and then slowly sat up. All of the kids laughed, including me. It was nice to see Tom get smashed for a change. Kaden's legendary status grew that day, but Tom's wounded pride needed to be mended. He staggered to his feet and began to run.

At first, his direction was erratic as he sought out his next victim. Then, his gaze turned towards Kotter and me.

"Oh, crap," I muttered.

Kotter and I turned and ran towards the swings, hoping to lose Tom in the confusion of swinging first-graders. Tom's course was undeterred. We ran to the slide, then the monkey bars, and then the tall slide. Tom was everywhere!

"Let's go to the bridge!" Kotter exclaimed.

We ran over to the wooden bridge, which connected the money bars to the spiral slide. Crouching low, we sat back to back, each scanning the playground for Tom.

"Where is he?" Kotter breathed in a hoarse voice.

"I don't know!" I cried in alarm.

A movement from above, on top of the bridge, caught our attention. We stood and looked up only to see Tom jump down and land right in front of me. His gorilla-like arms shoved me in the chest. I fell backwards, knocking Kotter down in the process. I landed on the wood chips of the playground with a thud, a muffled crunching noise catching my attention. My heart sank.

The playground supervisor blew a long whistle and waved her hand above her head. Recess was over.

"Ha ha, gotcha!" Tom exclaimed, a distorted look of triumph on his face. He turned and ran towards the school, fists pumping in the air.

"Are you OK, Matt?" Kotter asked, helping me up.

"Yeah, I think so."

I plunged my hand into my pocket and pulled out what was left of my glasses. My parents were going to kill me.

CHAPTER 5

"Do you want to tell them?" my dad asked my mom as we began to eat dinner. My mom had made tacos, so we were all busy trying to get the right amount of toppings in our shells.

"Sure!" my mom smiled as she paused from making her tacos. All of us kids looked at our mom, except Owen, who was pouring cheese on top of his taco meat.

"So your father and I have been talking about where to take the family in a few weeks for Memorial Day weekend. We decided we're going to take a trip down to Mesa Verde National Park in Colorado."

"What's there?" asked Will.

"I went there as a kid," my dad said. "There are cool cliff dwellings where the Anasazi lived a long time ago. We can explore the ruins and hike around the mountains there. It's one of the coolest places I've ever been."

"Sweet," I said.

"Where are we staying, and does it have a pool?" asked Rachel.

"We are staying at a hotel near the park," said my mom. "And yes, it has a pool and hot tub."

"How long will we be gone?" I asked.

"We'll take off on that Friday and then come back late Monday night, so you don't miss any school on that Tuesday," my dad said. "We'll also swing by Arches National Park on the way home. Trust me, this trip will be amazing!"

That night, I began to walk downstairs to get a drink, but stopped when I heard my mom ask my dad a question. I sat on the stairs where they couldn't see me and listened.

"What do you think is wrong with Matt?" she asked. I heard my dad shift around on the couch as he paused the show he was watching.

"It's a little weird that he keeps getting sick, but the doctors don't seem worried," he said.

"Yeah, but doesn't that concern you? Maybe it's because I'm his mom, but this is not normal. He's had these random headaches and fevers off and on over the last few months. He's even thrown up a couple of times. Maybe you haven't seen it because you have been traveling so much lately, but I'm starting to really second guess what the doctors are saying."

There was an awkward pause as I waited to hear what my dad was going to say. I hadn't really thought much about my health, but all of a sudden I started to feel a little worried.

"I don't know. I guess because the doctors haven't been worried, I haven't worried," my dad said. My dad can say some dumb things sometimes. Lucky for him, she ignored it.

"Seriously, sweetheart. I'm getting more concerned. Have you seen Matt's eyes lately? Sometimes I swear it looks like he is cross-eyed."

"What? I haven't noticed that at all."

"Just do me a favor and look at Matt's eyes when he gets back from school."

My eyes were crossed? I knew things were looking blurry, but that was because I had broken my glasses and wasn't wearing them. Somehow my parents hadn't noticed that part yet . . .

"Sure, of course. Tell you what, this trip to Mesa Verde is only two weeks away. When we get back from the trip, if Matt is still having weird symptoms, let's find a different doctor and get another opinion."

"Thank you," my mom said. I snuck back upstairs and laid down. Did my eyes really look crossed?

CHAPTER 6

The drive to Durango, Colorado, seemed like it took forever. The name sounded cool, though, like some old-time western town from the movies my dad liked to watch. Our hotel looked fun, and I could see it had an indoor pool. Even though it was almost June, it was still a little chilly outside. My dad was inside getting the hotel key while my mom was very focused on something she was reading on her phone. Rachel kept calling her name, but she wasn't answering.

"Mom!" Rachel almost shouted.

"What?" Mom asked, sounding a little annoyed.

"Can we go swimming after we check-in?" Rachel asked.

"Of course, but we need to eat dinner first."

"Ooh, what's for dinner?" I asked.

"Pizza," said Mom, studying her phone. She then looked up at me with a concerned face.

"Matt, where are your glasses? I don't think I have seen you wear them in a while," she asked me.

"Uh," I began, but was interrupted when Dad entered the van. That was close!

"OK, we are in room 127 over in the adjacent building," Dad said, handing a key card to Mom.

Mom smiled but looked very tired. I guess she was worn out after all the driving.

Our hotel had two bedrooms, which meant we could spread out a little.

"Matt and I get the bed!" Will said, running into one room.

"Mom, do I have to share a bed with Owen again?" Rachel complained.

"Yes, but it's only for a few nights," Mom said.

Mom began unpacking while Dad ran down the street to pick up a couple of pizzas. An hour later, we were ready to go swimming.

Will, Rachel, and I jumped into the heated swimming pool while Owen slowly walked down the steps into the warm water. He was wearing his lifejacket, which made him look super chubby. Dad was going to get in with us, but saw Mom walking over to sit down by the hot tub, so he went over there to talk to her.

"Let's play sharks and minnows!" Rachel said.

"I'll be the shark," said Will.

We played sharks and minnows for a while. Owen kept splashing on the stairs while my mom and dad talked. It looked like a really serious conversation. I think they were talking about me because they kept looking at me but tried not to act like they were looking at me.

I don't know what the big deal was. Things did look blurry to me, but that was probably because I wasn't wearing my glasses. I thought about telling them how they were broken, but thought I better wait until summertime, or maybe when school started again in the fall.

"Hey, Matt, let's get in the hot tub!" Rachel said.

"Good idea!"

We scrambled up the steps and walked quickly over to the hot tub. The water was steaming as we slid in and started the jets. It felt great to relax in the hot water. Mom and Dad were still talking nearby. Dad was looking really serious now too, and he kept shaking his head and moving his hands, like he was saying, "I don't know."

"Mom, Dad! Thanks so much for taking us here!" I said, smiling at them.

Mom tried to smile back at me, but I could see she was feeling sad.

"You're welcome," Dad said, smiling back. He turned to face Mom, and I could tell something was going on. What was bothering them so much?

CHAPTER 7

The canyon walls were so high above my head, I felt like I was stuck at the bottom of the deepest hole in all of Colorado. We walked all the way down to the bottom of the canyon to explore Spruce Tree House, an old Anasazi cliff dwelling. We are allowed to walk up to the walls in this ruin and even climb down a ladder into a kiva, which is a covered pit used for religious events. The walls of the ruins are made of adobe, which are basically old bricks that are now starting to crumble in spots. I can see why the Anasazi liked this place. There is water, shady green trees, and it is so well hidden, no one could ever know they lived here. The Anasazi lived on this mountain in Southwest Colorado for hundreds of years and then suddenly vanished around the year 1200. No one knows exactly why.

"Dad, didn't you say you came here as a kid?" I asked my dad as we walked down the trail by the ruins.

"Yep. I was about fourteen when grandma and grandpa took my siblings and me here. This is probably where my love for archaeology started."

"That's awesome," I respond, thinking about what it must be like to excavate a site like this one. "Didn't you study archaeology in college?"

"I did, though technically my degree is in anthropology."

"What's that?"

"It's the study of peoples and cultures. The difference is that anthropologists typically study living peoples and cultures while archaeologists study those who have passed on."

"Like dinosaurs!" I say, knowing how this bugs my dad. He smacked me playfully on the back of my head.

"No, dufus," he laughs, "that's paleontology, not archaeology."

We walked along the trail a little further and talked as my dad singled out various points of interest about the cliff dwellings. We decided to stop in the shade for a few minutes to drink some water and catch our breath.

"So Matt," my dad says loud enough to catch my mom's attention. "Where are your glasses?"

Crap. I had hoped they hadn't noticed or had at least forgotten.

"Um," I begin, my mind racing for a good excuse. "I broke them."

"You broke them?" my mom asked.

"Yeah . . ."

"How did that happen?" my dad asked flatly.

"I was playing on the playground and had them in my pocket."

"Why did you put them in your pocket?" my mom asked. My dad was trying to suppress a smile.

"Well, we were playing tag outside, and I didn't have time to run them back inside." I thought it sounded reasonable.

"So, you put them in your pocket?" Mom asked incredulously.

"I probably should have kept wearing them and not played tag."

"I just think it's amazing you could fit your glasses in your pocket. Usually, they are so stuffed with wrappers and paper that nothing else can fit," my dad said chuckling.

"OK, we'll go see the eye doctor when we get home," my mom said as she finished the rest of the water in her water bottle.

We spent the rest of the day exploring more ruins and learning all about the Anasazi culture. I thought the pottery they made was really cool. The pots were white or light tan with black lines all over them. Some even had shapes of turtles or lizards on them. We left the park around dinner time and headed back to the hotel. I could tell my mom was still feeling stressed about my health, but I really felt fine. I guess I didn't see what the big deal was. The only thing weird was that I was starting to see double now, but I figured that was because I broke my glasses.

The next day we drove to Moab, Utah, and hiked around the arches in the national park. I thought it was neat, but not as cool as the cliff dwellings. After spending the night in Moab, we drove home the next day. I was happy to be home. Summer break was coming quickly. I only had the rest of this week and all of the next one before I had the whole summer off to play around.

CHAPTER 8

I threw up again. I couldn't help it. It just happened so fast. I didn't feel sick, though, which was weird. It was Wednesday, and I really wasn't too upset that I had to go home. I just hoped Mom wouldn't take me to see the doctor. I was sitting in the school office when Mom walked in.

"Is everything OK with Matt?" the secretary asked my mom as she began to sign me out. I was sitting in a chair reading, pretending not to pay attention to what they were saying.

"I don't know," said Mom, sounding a little upset. "The doctors have no idea and keep saying that his random fevers are from some infection his body is fighting off."

"I hope you find an answer soon," said the secretary.

"Thank you," my mom said. "Matt, let's go."

I grabbed my backpack and followed Mom out the door. Maybe this meant I could play some video games?

"How does your tummy feel?" Mom asked me.

"Good."

"Did you start feeling sick before you threw up?" she asked as she sat down inside the minivan.

"No, I was just walking down the hall and just threw up all of a sudden," I replied as I buckled my seatbelt.

I don't know what the deal was, but I saw my mom gripping the steering wheel really tightly, like she was trying to wring out a wet dishcloth.

The next day, I got to stay home. I had an appointment with the eye doctor later that morning to see if I still needed glasses. My dad was not traveling this week, and I heard him walk upstairs from his basement office.

"Where's Mom?" he asked me.

"She's up in your room," I said, putting on my hoody.

"Jen?" he called.

"I'm coming," she said as she walked out of their room and down the stairs.

My dad hugged her. "Call or text me when you can," he said.

"I will," she said as we walked into the garage.

I liked going to Dr. Bowen's office because she had some cool magazines and books I could look at. She also had toys to play with, but only the really little kids played with those. I sat and flipped through an animal magazine while my mom was reading something on her phone. Owen sat in the chair next to Mom driving his toy cars along the armrest.

"Matt?" called a lady from the doorway dressed in scrubs. I always thought the scrubs they wore looked like pajamas. One day I hoped I could wear pajamas and get paid to do it.

"Come on, boys," Mom said, softly as she stood up.

We sat in the exam room for a few minutes, and then Dr. Bowen knocked and entered the room.

"Hi, Matt, I hear you broke your glasses." Dr. Bowen's energetic attitude made me smile. Even Mom seemed happy to see her.

"Yeah, I broke them a few weeks ago."

"Oh, no!" Dr. Bowen replied, pretending to be surprised. "Well, let's take a look at how your eyes are doing."

I sat in a special chair surrounded by lots of weird looking metal contraptions filled with lenses and dials. I was asked to start looking through one lens, then another. Dr. Bowen swapped the lenses and asked me to read a bunch of letters. After several minutes of testing, she looked at my mom.

"Well, it looks like Matt's eyes are OK. He still needs glasses, though. I'm going to go back into my office for a minute, but then I'll be right back, and we can get him fitted for new frames. If it helps any," she continued, looking at me, "you were going to need new glasses anyway. Your eyes have changed since the last time we met."

Dr. Bowen left, and Mom pulled out her phone and began texting. She didn't know it, but I snuck a look to see what she was texting.

I am so relieved, the doctor said Matt's eyes look good, she texted Dad.

That's great, glad to hear it! He texted back a few seconds later.

Dr. Bowen knocked and came back into the room, a serious look on her face.

"Matt, I want to look at your eyes again."

Mom gave her a concerned look. "Is something wrong?"

"I just need to double-check something quickly."

Dr. Bowen looked into my eyes again with one of her special tools. She started to look a little worried.

"Jen, I want you to take Matt to a specialist. Something doesn't look quite right, and I need a specialist to really look at his eyes."

"Should I be concerned?" Mom asked, a slight edge to her voice.

"I don't know, but the ophthalmologist should be able to make a better diagnosis. Call me after you have met with him."

The next day, both my mom and dad took me to the ophthalmologist. The doctor looked at me with another special looking tool and said I was "A-OK." I could tell my mom was really frustrated when we left.

"Something is wrong!" Mom whispered to Dad in the car, thinking I could not hear them, but hello, I was right behind them. We were driving home, and I pretended to not listen to them talk as I looked out the window. Adults are funny that way. Sometimes they think kids don't listen, then act surprised when we repeat back to them something they said.

"I don't get it," said my dad.

"I'm calling Dr. Bowen," my mom said as she pulled out her phone.

She dialed the number to Dr. Bowen's office and was placed on hold for a few minutes.

"This is Dr. Bowen," a voice said on the other end of the phone. The volume on Mom's phone was loud enough, so I could hear her voice.

"Hi, this is Jen Hales. We took Matt to the ophthalmologist today, and he said he did not see anything. What is going on?"

"Thank you for calling me. I could hardly sleep last night because of Matt. I don't know exactly what is going on here, but I feel like I need to tell you to go to the ER and request imaging."

I saw my mom flinch when Dr. Bowen said that.

"What's wrong?" Dad whispered. Mom held up one finger, telling him to wait a second.

"OK," Mom told Dr. Bowen, "so we just go in and say that you told us to come in and that Matt needs imaging."

"Yes, I'll call as soon as we hang up and let them know that Matt needs some imaging done. Good luck, I hope everything turns out OK. Let me know if they find anything."

"OK, thank you," said Mom as she hung up.

"We need to go to the ER," she told Dad, grabbing his arm and biting her lower lip.

CHAPTER 9

"OK, Matt, just lay down here and get comfortable. We are going to take some pictures of your brain," the technician said as she helped me up onto a platform. I was getting a CT scan, and everyone seemed to think this was a big deal.

I laid down on the platform and rested my head on the pillow. I was starting to feel a little nervous about all of this. What if they found something wrong?

"Now hold still. The platform is going to move a little, and you may hear a little noise, and that's normal. This will only take a few minutes."

I stared up at the ceiling and felt the platform move as my head entered a large donut-shaped device. The platform moved me a little bit, but after a few minutes, I was done.

"OK, Matt. Let's get you back to your mom," the technician said as she helped me off the platform. Was it me or did she look like she had seen a ghost?

We walked out the door to where my mom was waiting. She stood up as we walked out, looking from me to the technician.

"He did great," the technician said. "I'll walk you back to your room."

We weaved our way through the hallways until we came back to the ER room, where my dad was waiting.

"OK, the doctor will review the CT scan and be in soon," the technician said, closing the door behind her.

My parents kept looking at each other, like they were trying to read each other's minds. I jumped up on the exam table and heard the paper covering crinkle underneath me. I began to move around, just to hear it make noise. My parents were whispering in the corner while we waited for Dr. Collins, the ER doctor who was examining me, to come back in. We didn't have to wait long before there was a soft knock at the door.

"Mr. and Mrs. Hales?" Doctor Collins poked his head in through the doorway. "Can I speak with you outside for a minute?"

My mom and dad stood up and looked at me. Mom patted me on the shoulder.

"We'll be right back," she said as they walked out the door. They didn't close it all the way, so

I snuck over to look through the crack and listen to what they were talking about.

Dr. Collins had his back towards me, but I could hear him and kind of see my mom's face as she faced him. I saw his shoulders shrug as he took a deep breath before he spoke.

"Matthew has a brain tumor. It is large, and it looks like it has been there for a while," the doctor said.

Suddenly, my mom started to cry as her knees buckled. I remembered seeing Rachel's knees give out when she cut her finger. My dad and Dr. Collins helped her up and laid her on a nearby hospital stretcher.

"Can I see it, the CT image?" my dad asked, his voice sounding shaky.

"Sure, come here," Dr. Collins said, taking my dad into another room.

I couldn't see where they went, but through the crack in the door I could see the stretcher where my mom was laying down. What was a brain tumor? I had heard of tumors before, but I wasn't sure what they were. All I knew was that it had to be bad. I had never seen my mom cry like this before, and I had never heard my dad talk in such a shaky voice. Was I going to die?

A few minutes later, my dad and the doctor walked out and went over to where my mom was lying down. The doctor said a few more things to them that I couldn't hear then walked away.

"What did the doctor say while you were in there?" she asked.

"We need to take Matt to Primary Children's Hospital in Salt Lake City right away."

"Who is going to watch the other kids?"

"I'll make some calls to see who can watch them tonight."

"No, I can do that. I'll call my mom and let her know too. Maybe she can come out."

"Good idea. We need to tell Matt."

I walked back over to the exam table and quietly climbed back up. I didn't want them to know I had been spying on them. I looked around to find a magazine or something I could pretend to read. Nothing, except some celebrity magazine. Yuck.

My parents pushed the door open and looked like they had seen a ghost. My mom wasn't crying, but her eyes looked a little red and puffy.

"What's wrong, Mom?" I asked.

"Sweetie," she paused. "You have a brain tumor, and we need to go to Salt Lake so they can remove it."

"What's a brain tumor?"

"Basically, you have something inside your brain that doesn't belong there, and there is a surgeon in Salt Lake City who can do the surgery to remove it," said my dad. I could tell he was trying to make it sound like no big deal. But if it was no big deal, why were we going to Salt Lake City and not staying in Idaho Falls?

"I have to have surgery?" I asked, suddenly feeling scared. I was hoping I could take some medicine and maybe miss a few days of school.

"Yes," replied Mom. "But these surgeons are some of the best in the world."

"I don't want to go!"

"Bud, we don't have a choice," said Dad.

"I don't care!" I shot back. There was no way I was going to let anyone cut open my head.

"Matt," my dad began with a quiet voice, "Let's say a prayer first and go from there, one step at a time."

I nodded. We bowed our heads, and my dad said a prayer. We pray often as a family, but I had never heard a prayer like that one before. It was like my dad was begging his dad for help.

CHAPTER 10

My mom left my dad and me in the hospital to go home and pack some clothes. They thought we would be gone for a few days and wanted to be prepared since Primary Children's Hospital is about three hours away from our house. While mom was gone, my dad had to sign some forms, and the doctor and nurses started giving my dad all sorts of instructions. I just sat on the exam table, swinging my legs and hearing the paper crinkle as I moved. This was going to suck. I didn't want to go to Salt Lake City. I didn't want a brain tumor. And I definitely didn't want somebody cutting open my head.

After a long time, my mom returned as we walked out of the ER.

"Good luck," Doctor Collins said as he shook hands with my dad.

"Thank you," my dad said quietly as we climbed into the car.

"Hey, Matt," my mom said, turning around from the front passenger seat to look at me. "I brought a blanket and pillow in case you want to rest while we drive down."

"Thanks," I said, wrapping the blanket around my shoulders and laying down on the pillow. I wanted to sleep, or somehow pretend I wasn't having this nightmare. Eventually, I dozed off, but woke up when I heard my dad tell my mom we had crossed the border into Utah. My mom must have been resting because I heard her sit up in her seat and begin talking to my dad.

"Telling the other kids about Matt was hard," she began.

"Yeah, how did that go?" my dad asked, glancing back at me to make sure I was asleep. My eyes were closed, but I was listening as best I could.

"Well, I gathered the kids and had them sit down and told them I needed to tell them about Matt. Will looked worried, and Rachel could tell something was really wrong. Owen, of course, just kept playing with his toys."

Mom took a deep breath and continued. I slowly opened my eyes to peek at my dad, who was staring straight ahead at the road. It was hard to tell what he was thinking about.

"So I told them Matt was really sick and that he has a brain tumor, and you and I need to take him to Salt Lake City for surgery right away."

"How did they react to that?" Dad asked.

"So Will stood up and started pacing. He became a little teary-eyed too. Rachel started to cry when I said the word 'surgery' and Owen did something interesting."

"What did he do?" my dad asked, glancing over at Mom.

"Well, first, Rachel asked what brain tumor was. So I said that Matt has something in his brain that shouldn't be there. It's like a big owie, and that the doctor has to go in and remove the owie. Then, Owen stood up and came over and hugged my legs. I'll never forget what he said. He said, 'Mommy? I'm sad because you are sad.' When he said that, my heart just broke, but I didn't cry. I told him it's going to be OK."

"Wow, that's incredible that Owen would react like that," my dad said.

"Yeah, it really is. He's a good kid."

"Well, while you and Matt were sleeping for the last hour, I have been thinking and praying a lot."

"About Matt?"

"Of course," my dad said. "This has been hard to swallow for sure. I've doubted myself and blamed myself for not acting sooner."

"You can't do that. It wouldn't have changed anything."

"I know, but I can't help feeling that way," my dad said. "But as we came to the Malad Pass, I had a thought which was comforting."

"What was it?" my mom asked. I was curious too. I could use some comfort right about now.

"Well, recently at church, we heard the story in the Bible about when two men were walking on the road to Emmaus and a stranger joined them, asking why they were feeling so sad. They then told him that Jesus had been crucified. The stranger then began to quote and explain the scriptures to them. The men suddenly realized that the stranger was Jesus and that Jesus had been resurrected."

My dad stopped for a moment to gather his thoughts. My mom waited, and I opened an eye to see my dad. He looked blurry to me, but I could tell he was trying hard not to cry.

"As I saw the Malad Pass ahead of us, I thought that it kind of symbolized our own personal road to Emmaus, and if miracles happened back then, then maybe miracles can happen right now."

My mom grabbed my dad's hand, and I closed my eyes, trying hard to fall back asleep. I hoped miracles still happen today too.

CHAPTER 11

I woke up as we pulled into the parking garage of Primary Children's Hospital in Salt Lake City. *This sucks*, I thought, as my parents led me out of the car and into the hospital. The hospital walls had leaves painted in various shades of bright green, giving the appearance I was walking into a happy forest. Only I wasn't walking into a happy forest. I was heading to the emergency room to meet a doctor who was going to dig something out of my brain. I think I know what Han Solo must have felt before Darth Vader froze him in carbonite. I bet Han thought it sucked too.

My dad made a comment to my mom about how emergency rooms always seem busier on a Friday night. My mom went to the nurse behind the desk, who did not look like she was having a good night, and handed her the slip of paper the nurse at our ER had given her. As the nurse read the paper, her eyes softened as she looked back at my mom. My mom looked tired, more tired

49

than I had ever seen her look before. She said something to my mom, pointing to a corner of the waiting room.

"She told us to go sit over there," my mom said, leading us to where the nurse had pointed.

"Did she say how long of a wait it would be?" my dad asked.

"No," my mom replied, sitting down heavily. Her shoulders were sagging, but she was trying to keep a smile on her face for me.

"Can I go to the bathroom?" I asked.

"Sure, bud, it's over there," my dad said, pointing across the waiting room.

I took my time returning from the bathroom, stopping to look at the fish in a saltwater tank. *I bet fish don't get brain tumors,* I thought, wishing I was swimming in the ocean and not stuck in some crummy ER hours away from home. Looking around me, I saw other kids sitting with their parents. Some kids were crying, others were bandaged up. One boy, probably close to my age, had a big bloody bandage around his arm. I bet he had a cool story to tell. Another kid was holding ice to his mouth, probably not feeling the blood oozing through his lips. I wasn't sure if I was jealous of those kids or if I felt sorry for them. Maybe it was a little of both. Eventually, I wandered back to my parents, who had obviously been talking about something but had decided to stop their conversation when I got back.

"How are you feeling?" my mom asked.

"Bored," I said, not trying to hide my feelings.

"Here, you can play some games on my phone while we wait."

I tried playing some of my favorite games, but I couldn't enjoy myself too much. I just wanted to get home. I would play one game for a few minutes, then switch to another and then another. None of them seemed fun anymore.

"Matthew?" a nurse called, ending my gaming session.

We all stood to follow the nurse into a special room.

"Come make yourselves comfortable in here," the nurse instructed, pointing us to more chairs. At least these chairs were more comfortable, and we didn't have to hear all the crying babies in the waiting room.

"A child life specialist will be with you shortly," the nurse said as she closed the door behind her.

My dad raised an eyebrow at my mom, which he usually did when he thought something was odd. My mom gave a brief shrug and shook her head, which meant she had no idea what to expect either. She didn't have to wait long. There was a light knock on the door before it was opened by a woman who quietly came inside and greeted us.

"Hi, my name is Anne," she said, shaking my mom and dad's hands. "And you must be Matt," she smiled at me.

"Yeah," I said, looking at her expectantly.

"Does he know what is going on?" she asked quietly, casting sideways glances at my parents.

"Yes," my mom replied. I could sense the sadness in her voice as she clutched her hands in her lap.

"Matt, what kind of toys do you like?"

I didn't expect that question. "I don't know. Legos?" *Really?* I thought. *Legos are the best thing I can think of?*

"OK, I'll be back in a minute," she said as she disappeared through the door. She returned with a brand new city themed Lego set. I didn't see that one coming either. She explained to my parents that many families donate toys to the hospital for kids like me to play with to help them stay calm throughout their time in the hospital.

"Go ahead and open them if you like. I want to talk with you about your tumor if that's OK," she spoke softly.

I nodded as I opened the box and began building the new set. I really prefer the superhero-themed Legos, but the city themed set Anne gave me was cool too. One of the guys even came with a boat.

"So Matt, do you know what a brain tumor is?"

"It's something stuck in my head that they have to cut out," I said, never taking my eyes off the Legos. Who has time to talk when there is a new Lego set to build?

"That's right. Do you know how they are going to remove it?"

I realized I didn't know. I set the Legos down and turned to face her.

"No. How?" I asked suspiciously.

She pulled out a small doll made of fabric. It kind of looked like an oversized gingerbread man wearing a hospital gown.

"Well first, they have to give you an IV," she said as she pulled a large needle from the basket she carried. "Do you think you can stick this needle in the doll's arm?"

I grabbed the needle and jabbed it in the doll's arm, then looked at Anne to see what I should do next.

"Good! Now take some of this tape and tape it down so it can't fall out." Anne handed me a small roll of medical tape, which was covered with some sort of checkered pattern.

I did as she said and surveyed my work. Not too bad. That needle was not going anywhere.

"Do you know why you need an IV?" she asked.

I shook my head. "Why?"

"The IV helps the doctors and nurses put fluid and medicine directly into your body. It stings for a second, but then it's not too bad. When we get you upstairs in a few minutes, the nurse will put an IV into your arm. Is that OK?"

"Yeah, I guess," I shrugged.

I turned back to my Legos and started to find the next piece for the boat I was building.

"Matt, do you know how they are going to remove your tumor?"

Another good question. I stopped searching for the piece and turned to look at Anne. I was less sure I wanted to know the answer to this question.

"No . . ."

"The doctors are going to put some special medicine into your IV, which will make you fall asleep. While you are asleep, they are going to make a cut on your head, find the tumor, take it out, and then stitch you back up. When you wake up, you'll have a big bandage on your head."

That sounded simple enough.

"OK," I said. I paused, waiting to see if she was done.

"Here, Matt," she said, handing me a black marker. "Take this marker and draw a face on the doll."

I didn't practice drawing very much, though my parents liked to laugh at a video of me as a toddler coloring all over myself with markers. I guess I wanted to have some cool tattoos or something like that back then. I held the doll with my left hand as I traced two eyes, a nose, and mouth on the face of the doll. I then made some scribbles on the top of the head to make it look like hair.

"Excellent!" she said encouragingly. "Now, can you draw a line on the head where the doctor is going to go in and take out the tumor?"

I took the marker and drew a line across the top of the forehead near the hair.

"Like this?" I asked.

"Perfect, now can you draw stitches on the line?"

I had seen enough Frankenstein pictures to know what stitches looked like, and once at a family reunion a few years ago I had slipped and hit the back of my head. It took about seven stitches to stop the bleeding. I added perpendicular short lines along the length of the first line I drew to make it look like one big stitch across the top of the doll's head.

"Good job! Now, there is one last thing," she said as she produced a gauze bandage with some tape. "Can you wrap the doll's head in this bandage and tape it in place?"

I grabbed the gauze and wrapped the head. When I was done, I thought it looked really good. The doll smiled back at me with its black marker smile. I figured this surgery would be easy, and I would be home in no time.

"Awesome," said Anne. "I want you to remember this as you get ready for surgery. They are going to take really good care of you."

Anne turned and started speaking in hushed tones with my parents, who nodded a lot and asked a few questions. I ignored all the grown-up talk and focused on building my Lego boat. This hospital is not so bad, after all.

My hospital room smelled clean, like our house does after my mom has done her regular deep cleaning. As I sat in my hospital bed, the room looked bright with lights all over the ceiling and even some in the walls. There was a flatscreen TV with a DVD player on the wall in front of me and several computer monitors, tubes, and rubbery wires behind me, somewhat out of sight. My dad had brought in our luggage and had stashed it in the far corner so it would not interfere with anything or anyone. The TV remote was attached to my bed, and I began looking for a show to watch. Before I had even found something, there was a knock at my door.

A short, athletic-looking man dressed in green hospital scrubs walked in. He looked to be about my dad's age, though he had a little bit of gray hair poking out from under his surgical hat. Several other people walked in behind him.

"Hi, I'm Dr. Benetti," he said with a wide grin, shaking hands with my parents and then me. "You must be Matthew."

I nodded, not sure what to think of this doctor, though I could tell I would like him.

"I am the Head Resident of Neurosurgery and will be assisting Dr. Rockhouse in your surgery. He'll be in here in a few minutes." He paused before continuing. "Let me just say that it is good you came here when you did. You would not have wanted to wait any longer to get this removed."

My dad shifted uneasily in his chair. The doctor took a deep breath, and with a slight grin, he continued.

"We've looked at your images, and the tumor is on your basal ganglia. So pretend you draw a line straight down from the top of your head and another one going right between your eyes."

Dr. Benetti hung his left pointer finger above the crown of my head and his right pointer finger hovered inches in front of my face pointing right between my two crossed eyes.

"That spot where these imaginary lines would intersect is about where your tumor is. So tomorrow, we are going to do some more imaging and take some measurements, then on Sunday morning, we are going to take that thing out. Does that sound like a plan?"

I nodded, more interested in the Xbox I just noticed sitting by the DVD player. We only had a Wii at home, and I was dying to try the Xbox. At that moment, a tall thin man in green scrubs walked in.

"Hi, I'm Dr. Rockhouse," said the man as he shook hands with my parents.

"Can you tell us anything else about the tumor?" my dad asked. There was an edge in his voice I had never heard before. He sounded worried, even anxious. Dr. Benetti took a deep breath before responding.

"We can't tell anything for sure, but based on the location and the shape, we think this tumor is benign."

My parents both let out a large breath of air at the same time, almost like they had been having a contest to see who could hold their breath the longest. I sometimes did that with Rachel, especially when we drove through tunnels in our car.

"That's good to hear," my dad said, looking over at my mom. I could see tears starting to well up in my mom's eyes, but these tears were not sad. She seemed happy and relieved.

"Keep in mind, though," said Dr. Rockhouse, "we grade brain tumors on a scale, types 1 and 2 being considered benign while types 3 and 4 are malignant. We think Matt's tumor is a one or two, but we won't know for sure until we operate."

The doctor talked with my parents for a little while longer, but I didn't really care about what they said. For the first time all day, my parents were kind of smiling. I guess the news was good.

As the nurse left, she asked if she could get me anything.

"What games do you have for the Xbox?"

"Let me go get them. I'll be right back."

A few minutes later, she returned with a basket full of Xbox games. There were tons I could choose from, most of which I had never played. After rummaging for a few minutes, I pulled out a fishing game, which made my dad smile.

"I'll try this one," I said, pulling the game from the basket.

"OK, have fun!" the nurse said as she left the room.

"Dad, do you want to play?" I asked.

"Sure! This looks awesome."

My dad hates video games, mostly because he is terrible at them. He once told me that even as a kid, he was never very good. I was glad he wanted to play, though. He mostly watched me play and talked to me. My mom rested on the sofa in the room, watching both of us with a smile on her face. I could tell she was tired, but at least now she seemed relaxed. This was turning out to be a pretty cool day.

CHAPTER 12

The next day, Saturday, was super boring for the most part. Nurses kept coming in and checking my vitals, which meant they had to check my pulse, how often I was breathing, and my blood pressure. I also had to have some MRI's done, which is when I lay inside a large machine that makes a lot of noise. The machine takes pictures of my brain using magnets. I'm not sure how that works, but I was able to wear some cool goggles that played a movie for me while they did the MRI. I made it about halfway through a superhero movie before it was over.

The highlight of the day was when my teacher, Mrs. Ball and her husband Doug, showed up with some hamburgers and fries. Doug sometimes showed up at school with donuts for our class, so we called him Doug the Donut Man. We all ate down in the lobby and talked as we chowed down on the food.

"Matt, I brought you a gift!" Mrs. Ball said with her usual high level of energy.

"Really?" I asked.

"Here you go," said Doug, handing me a large stuffed black bear.

"Awesome, thank you!"

"That's very kind of you, Michelle," my mom said to Mrs. Ball.

"It's the least we can do. I have just been worried sick about Matt," she said. "Here, I brought something for you and Jason too." Mrs. Ball handed my mom a large brown grocery bag full of food.

"Thank you," said my mom. "This is too much!"

"Don't worry about it," said Doug. "We're glad we were in the area and could stop by."

"Were you running a race?" my dad asked.

Doug nodded, and the two of them began talking about running. I heard Doug say something about it being his birthday. Spending your birthday in a hospital would really suck. My mom talked with Mrs. Ball while I enjoyed the hamburger. It was really good, and it was nice to see Mrs. Ball. We spent about an hour together in the lobby before Doug and Mrs. Ball had to leave.

"Can we come sit with you for a while tomorrow while Matt is in surgery?" Michelle asked my mom.

"Of course, it would be great to have you," my mom said.

"Matt, buddy, what are you thinking about?" my mom asked. It was getting late in the evening, and I was getting tired.

"Nothing," I lied. I was freaking out inside because they were cutting open my head in the morning and pulling something out of my brain!

"Matt, you look like you are shaking a little," my mom said as she came over to the hospital bed. It was just the two of us in the room since my dad was somewhere taking a shower.

"I'm just nervous. I don't want to have surgery."

"Matt, this is a good thing. The doctors know what they are doing."

My mom looked at me and brushed some of my hair back. Her hand felt comforting on my head.

"Tell you what," she said excitedly. "Can I read a book to you?"

"Sure," I said.

"Any preference?"

"Um, how about *Mr. Klutz is Nuts!*" I said. The *My Weird School* series was one of my favorites.

"I think that is an excellent choice," my mom said, pulling it out of her bag.

She sat down beside me on the bed and began to read. I leaned my head on her shoulder and tried to relax. I had a hard time focusing on the story.

"Matt, what's the matter?" Mom asked.

"Nothing," I lied.

"Are you nervous about tomorrow? You keep fidgeting."

"Yeah. I just don't want to have surgery. Can't I just take some medicine?" I plead.

"Sweetheart, I know this is scary, but it's going to be OK." She paused for a moment. "Do you want to say another prayer together?"

I nodded.

"Would you like to say it or do you want me to?"

"I'll say it," I said. I prayed I could sleep and that everything would be OK in the morning. It wasn't a long prayer, but I was too nervous to really say anything else.

"Did that help?" Mom asked.

"A little. Can you read some more?"

"Of course."

My mom continued reading our book. I leaned my head back on her shoulder and eventually, I drifted off to sleep.

I woke up Sunday morning when the nurse knocked on the door. The knock woke my dad up too, but my mom looked like she had been awake for a while.

The nurse walked in and opened the chart in her hands with my name on it.

"I'm just going to get your vitals," she whispered to me even though we were all awake. I guess if you work at night, you just get used to whispering a lot. "I'm about to go home," she told my mom, "but my replacement is almost here. She'll come in and get Matt ready and then he will be off to surgery."

"When is the surgery scheduled?" asked Mom.

"They want to start by eight o'clock, so I imagine they'll come and get him in about half an hour."

My mom glanced at her phone to check the time, then stood and stretched. It was almost seven o'clock.

"I'm going to freshen up really quick," she told my dad and me, then headed into the bathroom.

"How did you sleep last night?" my dad asked me.

"Good," I said, still feeling a little tired.

"Well, it'll be good to get this over with," my dad said. "You're going to do great."

"How soon can I eat? I'm kind of hungry right now," I said.

"Well, we'll have to wait and see what the doctor says," my dad replied.

"Dad, I don't want to have surgery."

"Matt," my dad took a deep breath and sat at the foot of my bed. "Everything is going to be OK. Your mom and I believe in miracles, and that is exactly what we are praying for today. Did you know that there are probably hundreds of people praying for you today?"

"Really?" I asked.

"Yep. Grandma and Grandpa Hales told me that everyone at their church is fasting and praying for you. Same with Grandma Larsen's church. There are even people in Europe and South America who know our family that are also praying and asking their friends to pray too."

"Whoa," I said, not really sure what to think.

"Seriously, Matt. Miracles still happen."

The pre-op room was super bright with nurses running around everywhere getting kids ready for surgery. I heard a small baby crying in the corner as the nurse was finishing its preparation for surgery. At this distance, everything was still kind of blurry, but I could hear the noise all around me. My mom sat on the bed beside me.

"Are you ready?" she asked me with a smile that looked like she was trying hard not to cry.

"Yeah," I answered, but the truth is I felt scared.

"Matt, it's going to be OK," said my dad. "Just remember what we talked about."

"Good morning, Matt!" said a tall man dressed in scrubs. "I'm Dr. Appleton, and I'll be putting you to sleep for your surgery. Does that sound good?"

I nodded, unsure of what to say. Nothing about this sounded good.

The doctor pulled up a roller stool and began asking my mom and me tons of questions. They were all the same questions everyone had been asking me for the last few days. How long had I been experiencing symptoms? On a scale of 1 to 10, how would I rate my pain? Is my vision blurry? Blah, blah blah.

"Alright, Matt! Let's do this," Doctor Appleton beamed.

"No, I'm not ready!" I shot back, shifting in my bed, looking for an escape. I needed to get out of here right away!

"This will help out," the doctor softly spoke, putting something in my IV.

And then, my head felt light, and everything turned to black.

CHAPTER 13

My eyes fluttered open, and the light was bright. I didn't know where I was or what was going on. In fact, I felt nothing at first.

"It's OK, Matt, you are waking up in the hospital. You just had surgery," a woman's voice said as she moved around my head out of view. Suddenly, I felt some panic set in. Surgery?! Then I remembered the last few days and something about a brain tumor. I needed to get out of this place, whatever this place was.

"Get these stupid things off me!" I yelled, pulling at restraints, which bound my wrists to the hospital bed.

"Matt, do you like to read?" asked the nurse, trying to sound calm.

Do I like to read? What kind of question was that?

"Yes," I said, uncertain why she was asking me.

"Good, what kind of books do you like to read?" she asked very politely. I felt I was being drawn into some sort of trap. I wasn't in the mood to play any games.

"I like to read books about how I can get OUT OF HERE!"

Even I was surprised that I yelled. At that moment, I heard my mom and dad chuckling as they walked into the room. This was the first time I really saw where I was. I was in a room with glass doors, various curtains, and a lot of light. More nurses came in to help out. I heard someone say something about me being in the ICU as they began talking to my parents.

One nurse, a large bald man with a beard and name tag, which read "Dave," pulled a syringe out of his chest pocket and added the medicine to my IV. A few moments later, everything felt quiet. I wasn't asleep, but I didn't feel fully awake, either.

"My name is Dave, and I'll be taking care of Matt this afternoon. We'll let him rest for a while, and then I'll be back in to check on him."

I saw my parents nod and thank him as he walked out. My mom walked over to me and gave me a kiss on the forehead.

"I'm so grateful this is all done," she whispered silently.

"Me too," I heard my dad say. I tried to nod, but I felt too tired to do anything.

I closed my eyes for a moment. I just needed a little more sleep.

"Matt?" I hear my mom say. "Are you doing OK?"

"I feel good, but my head hurts," I said as I woke up. I wasn't sure how long I had been out. I kind of remembered coming out of surgery, but I wasn't sure if it had been a bad dream.

"I bet it does! The doctor came by and said he thinks they got it all out," Mom replied.

"Good," I said groggily.

"Hey, bud," Dad said, walking over to the bedside.

"Hi, Dad."

"Feeling tired?"

"Yeah," I yawned.

"Here's the stuffed bear from Mrs. Ball," Mom said, showing me the large stuffed black bear and placing it in my bed.

"Thank you," I said, pulling the bear in close.

Mom just smiled and kept stroking my hair and face. Most of my head was covered in a bandage, but she found a few pieces of hair poking through the bottom of the wrapping. My dad just watched my mom as she kept stroking my hair and bandaged head so softly that I could barely feel it. Suddenly, my mom looked scared.

"Matt?" she said in alarm.

"Huh?" I replied. I tried to look at her, but my eyes wouldn't move.

"Look at me," she said with the kind of firmness, which made my dad turn to her in alarm. My dad leaned over to look me in the eyes. I could see him, and he also seemed worried. What was going on? I was trying to talk, but nothing was coming out of my mouth.

"Matt!" Mom yelled while rubbing my chest with her hand. "Sweetheart," she said, turning to my dad, "he is not responding! Go get the nurse!"

I was trying to respond, but nothing was coming out of my mouth, and I couldn't really move either.

After a few moments, I heard Dave walk in my room.

"Excuse me," he said, stepping close to me. He bent his large head down to look me in the eyes.

"Matt?" Dave asked, "Can you hear me?"

I could, but I couldn't respond. It was like I was trapped in my own body.

"I'm going to grab the doctor on the floor," Dave said, leaving the room. Moments later, several doctors and nurses entered the room and surrounded me. The doctor, a thin woman with dark hair and a slight accent, began assessing me by squeezing my hands and asking me to squeeze back. I tried but couldn't really do it.

"How long has he been like this?" the doctor asked my mom and dad.

"Just a few minutes," my dad managed with a wavering voice. Mom sat beside him, her fists clenched in a ball as she stared at me. I could see them, but that was about all I could do. The doctor turned and left the room for a few moments.

"He was here one minute and then, gone," Mom spoke softly to Dad, her voice sounding heavy.

"Do you think he is having a seizure?" my dad asked, squeezing her hand.

"I think so."

My dad took a deep breath, then slowly exhaled.

The doctor returned with more nurses, and they all started checking monitors and fussing all around me. I felt some pressure in my wrist as they pushed some medicine through my IV. The medical team continued to work all around me, then the doctor asked me to squeeze her hand, which I was finally able to do. A few minutes later, I could move my eyes, and then my tongue. I finally started to feel normal again.

"Matt should be OK, now," the doctor told my parents. "He had a seizure, which is normal after brain surgery. It's like his brain just needed to reboot."

CHAPTER 14

I get to eat all the cheeseburgers with fries and milkshakes that I want. My parents told me I was still in the hospital, but it felt like a hotel, just with lots of monitors and wires everywhere. I don't really remember waking up in the ICU, but I do remember seeing my parents and how they kept smiling at me. My mom won't leave me alone. Even my dad doesn't seem to want to leave.

The pain in my head was intense, but as long as I kept getting my medicine, it was OK. My days in the hospital were relaxing. For the first day or two, I was only allowed to lay down and watch TV. It was awesome! I never get to do that. And I got to eat more cheeseburgers. My mom read more of the *My Weird* School books to me, and we even started reading the *Michael Vey* series. A couple of days after surgery, I was allowed to go down and play in the hospital gym. My dad used to work at a hospital during college, and in those days, he would take people from surgery back to their hospital rooms. He was really good at driving the bed and wheelchair and liked to do wheelies with me when the nurses weren't looking.

Gym time was fun because I was able to throw and catch balls with my mom and dad. We also played pool as a family, and they had art tables where my mom and I could paint. Everyone kept looking at me, telling me what a good job I was doing. I didn't see what the big deal was. These were things I always did before the stupid tumor came anyway.

When my mom and dad thought I was either sleeping or watching TV, I could hear them talking to each other. I could tell they were waiting on something called a "pathology report." Evidently, that was a big deal. I wasn't sure what it meant, but when Dr. Rockhouse entered the hospital room on the Thursday after my surgery, I could tell my parents were anxious to hear the news.

"Matt, how are you doing?" the tall doctor asked me.

"Fine."

"Hold out your hands for me," the doctor asked. He proceeded to do a neuro check, which is something the nurses and residents had been doing with me several times a day since my surgery. It usually meant I had to squeeze fingers, touch my nose, and do a few other things, which made me look ridiculous.

"It looks like you are doing good!" he smiled. Then he turned towards my parents.

"Well, we got Matt's pathology report, and I want to share that with you."

He paused, waiting to see if my parents had any questions. Probably not since they were barely breathing.

"Matt had a type 2 pilomyxoid astrocytoma. It was about the size and shape of a small apricot, and I'm confident we got all of it out. In looking at the post-op MRI, though, it is hard to say as there is still a lot of swelling and bleeding."

"Can you say that name again?" my mom asked, grabbing a pen and paper.

"Pilomyxoid astrocytoma," replied the doctor as my mom wrote it down.

He paused again, and this time my dad had a question.

"So, was it benign like you originally thought?"

Dr. Rockhouse leaned back and took a deep breath.

"Like I think I said before Matt's surgery, benign and malignant are different with brain tumors than they are with other types of tumors. We rate brain tumors on a scale of 1 to 4, 1 and

2 generally being considered benign while 3 and 4 are generally considered malignant. It is probably better to think of them in terms of being aggressive. So while Matt's tumor wasn't super aggressive since it grew slowly, we rated it a type 2 because of its size and location."

My mom and dad nodded their heads.

"We also did a genetic test and wanted to let you know this type of tumor is not genetic."

"So, there is no concern this could happen to our other kids or his kids one day?" my mom asked.

"Nope," the doctor said. Then with a smile, he added while turning towards me, "Matt, you are one in a million!"

That made everyone in the room smile.

"Any questions?" he asked.

My mom began asking him more questions about what I should eat, what I can do, blah blah blah. By this point, I just wanted to turn the TV back on. Why did my dad always turn the TV off when a doctor came in? Suddenly, something the doctor said caught my attention.

"Probably Saturday," the doctor said.

"Wait, what?" I asked.

"Assuming everything goes well, we can take you home on Saturday," my mom said.

That was the best news I had heard all day.

I sat in the hospital bed thinking about what the doctor had said about my tumor. I wondered what it looked like, and how hard it was to remove. I sipped the last of my milkshake when I noticed my mom was staring at me.

"What are you thinking about, Matt?" she asked.

"Nothing," I said.

"Really?"

"Well, I was kind of thinking about the tumor and wondering what it looked like. Did they keep it?"

"Sort of. They kept some of it to do some additional testing. Your tumor is so rare that there isn't a ton of information out there about it."

"Wow, that's kind of crazy," I said, finishing off the milkshake. The hospital knows how to make milkshakes. I'm going to miss having these every day.

"I'm going to name it Pilo," I said.

"What?" my mom asked. My dad looked up from the magazine he was reading to see what was going on.

"My tumor," I grinned. "I'm naming it Pilo."

"Why are you naming your tumor?" my dad asked, trying to hold back a smile. Mom was trying to hold back a smile too.

"I don't know. I can't say that big long name, but Pilo is easy to remember," I said.

Mom smiled.

"Then Pilo it is," she said, taking my empty cup from me.

For some reason, giving the tumor a name gave it an identity to me. It had been a part of me, and while I was glad it was gone and I never wanted it to return, it was a part of my life and made me different from the other kids. And as my mom always said, being different makes you special.

After more tests, more imaging, more books, and more cheeseburgers, Saturday finally came, and I was once again in the backseat of our car, but this time heading home.

"Anyone hungry?" my dad asked from the driver's seat.

"Me!" my mom and I said together.

"Matt, what sounds good?"

"Um, how about In 'N Out?"

My dad smiled, "In 'N Out it is!"

After a few more minutes on the freeway, my dad exited, and we entered the restaurant. People were staring at my head, which was partially shaved across the top with black stitches in a curved S shape. The rest of my hair was sticking up everywhere. Even I thought I looked kind of freaky.

We ordered, then sat outside. The warm sun felt awesome after being stuck inside the hospital for a week. After a few minutes, my dad brought out the food.

"Dig in!"

I peeled back the waxy paper holding my double-double together and sunk my teeth into the soft bun. The flavor explosion in my mouth shocked my taste buds. Suddenly, the cheeseburgers of the hospital were a distant memory. Ever since that day, no other cheeseburger has ever tasted so good.

"So, Matt," my mom began in as she dipped her fries into fry sauce. I could tell by her tone she had something important to say but wanted to keep it light. "When we get home, you are going to have to take it easy."

She looked at me, trying to gauge my response. I stared back, willing her to continue.

"Do you know what that means?" she asked.

"Yeah," I said, chewing a mouthful of heaven. "It means I have to be careful."

My dad smiled. He had his sunglasses on, so it was hard to read his expression. He kept eating as my mom continued.

"It means you can't jump on the tramp, no skateboard or scooter, and no bike riding."

"No bike?" I said in alarm. "Why can't I ride my bike?"

"You might hurt your head," said my dad, giving my mom a break so she could eat.

"How could I hurt my head when I ride my bike? All I do is pedal."

"Well," said my dad grabbing a bunch or crispy fries and dunking them in fry sauce, "how did you get that scar on your ear?"

I had forgotten about that accident. A year or two ago, I had been out riding my bike and goofing off. Somehow my bike crashed, and I landed on top of it. The rubber guard on my handlebar was worn out, so when my ear landed on the handlebar, the metal edge ripped a gash in my earlobe. It took a few stitches to put it back together.

"Oh yeah. But I will be more careful!" I begged.

"Sorry, pal," my mom interjected. "No bike."

"Man, this summer already sucks."

CHAPTER 15

The drive home felt like the longest three hours of my life. I was going to miss the hospital food and all the nice people there, but I was really excited to be home. Finally, my dad turned the car onto our street.

"Holy cow," my dad said.

"What?" I asked as I leaned forward to see what he was looking at.

"Look at all the people!" he said.

"Whoa," I gaped. Our driveway was full of people from the neighborhood. Some people had made signs, and one of my friend's mom was making cotton candy on a table she had set up. My dad couldn't pull into the driveway with all the people there, so he just pulled up along the curb.

My mom rubbed her eyes. I wasn't sure why she was crying, but I could tell she was happy. This was the first time I think she cried since we were in the ER over a week ago. I guess she had let the tears all build up, and now they had to go somewhere.

"So, how ya doin, buddy?" Kotter asked, placing his arm around me.

"Good," I said, not sure what else to say. All sorts of kids from the neighborhood were gathering around and looking at me. I probably looked a little scary with a partially shaved head and lots of stitches. But no one was pointing or making fun of the way I looked. Instead, they all seemed happy to see me.

"Matt!" Rachel said as she gave me a hug. "I'm so glad to see you!"

I smiled back, not really sure what to say. Some of the other boys in the neighborhood came over and gave me a fist bump or high five. My dad was talking with the other dads while my mom talked with my grandma. I guess I hadn't realized that my grandma Larsen was here after flying all the way in from South Carolina.

"Matt, do you want to play?" Kotter asked.

"Sure, what do you want to do?"

"I don't know. It's the first day of summer break. I'm sure we can find something to do."

CHAPTER 16

The summer break was turning out to be OK. I couldn't ride my bike or jump on the trampoline, but I could run around, play video games, and go over to friends' houses. My head no longer hurt, and my vision was back to normal, but I did get tired pretty easy. Aside from the crazy scar on my head, it was almost like the brain tumor had never happened. At lunchtime, about a month after, we returned home, my dad came upstairs from his office and began talking to my mom as she made lunch. I was laying on the couch watching a nature show and could hear them talking.

"Hey Jen, what would you think if I took Will and Matt hiking up Mount Washburn?" That caught my attention. We hiked that mountain in Yellowstone National Park a couple of years ago, and it was tons of fun.

"I think that is a good idea, if you think Matt is ready for it," she replied cautiously.

"I think he is," Dad responded, sounding confident.

The following Saturday, the three of us jumped in the car and headed north towards the park. A couple of hours later, we arrived at the trailhead. Mount Washburn is a 10,243-foot peak in the northeast corner of the park. The summit is over three miles from the trailhead, and the trail is steep in some parts. I was so excited to be doing something new and exciting this summer.

"Are you boys ready?" my dad asked as he shrugged on his daypack.

"Yep," said Will as he started up the trail. I nodded and followed after him as my dad smiled at us.

"How are you doing, Matt?" my dad asked between breaths. We were nearing the summit, and my dad had to keep stopping to wait for me. I wasn't trying to be slow, but I just got so tired sometimes. Will was ahead of us on the trail, watching us and waiting until we were ready to follow him.

"I'm OK, I'm just tired," I smiled. I really was fine. In fact, I was more than fine. This was the most fun I had had all summer. It just took me longer than normal to hike the mountain.

"OK, we are almost to the top. We'll rest longer when we get there. Can you make it?" my dad asked.

"Yeah, I can make it," I said as I looked up at the summit.

The last part of the trail brought us out of the trees and offered an amazing view of the countryside. I could see forever. Ravens rode the thermals around us as sunlight reflected off the weather station on the summit. Years ago, the first time we hiked this trail, my dad had read that there was a water fountain at the summit inside the weather station, only when we got there, no water was to be found anywhere. We were dying of thirst but made it back to the van OK. This time, my dad had brought a bunch of water. We entered the weather station and sat on a bench taking in the view. It felt good to rest, drink some water, and eat some food. After about twenty minutes of rest, everyone started feeling ready to head back.

"Ready?" my dad asked Will and me. I think he could sense our readiness.

"Yep," said Will, rising from the bench where he was sitting. I nodded and stood with him. My dad looked at me like he was trying to guess if I could make it or not. There was no way I was going to give up. I had walked all the way up, and I was going to walk all the way down.

We stopped often on the descent. I think Will could probably have just run down the trail. It took us nearly two hours of walking and stopping before we finally arrived at the trailhead. I felt completely exhausted and flopped into the back seat. I was asleep before my dad even left the parking lot.

CHAPTER 17

I had never been so excited to get back to school. Last week, before school started, my mom and dad took me back to the hospital in Salt Lake to have my first follow up MRI. They seemed really nervous, but I didn't think it was a big deal. Aside from still being a little tired, I felt normal. I was glad to finally be rid of all the headaches and eyestrain. The doctor told us my MRI looked good, but that he wanted to have another one before Christmas. That sounded good to me. All I cared about was stopping by In-N-Out Burger on the way home. That place is so good!

I walked into school on the first day of class and saw a lot of people I knew. I found out that over the summer, there had been a lot of rumors about what had happened to me. Most people knew I had had a brain tumor, but there were a few people who hadn't heard that. Some people heard that I died, others heard that I couldn't see or speak. But everyone stared at the S-shaped scar on my head. I thought it looked cool, and so did a lot of my friends.

And then Tom arrived.

"Hey, I heard you were dead," Tom smirked.

"Nope, I'm still here," I said, trying to keep it light.

"So what, they pulled out part of your brain?"

"Just the tumor," I answered, hoping this would end soon.

"So, what kind of tumor was it?"

"A pilomyxoid astrocytoma," I said, hoping the technical name would confuse him, and we could move on. I had been practicing the word all summer just to get it right.

"A what?" he stammered.

"It was just a brain tumor. I got to get to class," I said, ducking past him. It seemed Tom had grown a little over the summer and added a few pounds.

"See you at recess!" Tom laughed. I wondered if he had been dreaming about playground tag all summer.

A massive game of tag was underway as Kotter, and I entered the playground. Kids ran everywhere to escape the person who was 'it,' reminding me of little baitfish trying to escape a shark. It was not hard to pick Tom out in the crowd. He was nearly a full head taller than most the kids and still seemed to enjoy shoving people when it was his turn to be 'it.'

"What do you think, do you feel up to playing?" Kotter asked me.

"Definitely," I said as we trotted out into the crowd.

"Who is 'it'?" asked Kotter to a random boy running by.

"Who do you think?" he yelled back, pointing in the direction he just left. There was no mistaking the look in Tom's eyes. It only took him a second to zero in on me.

"Hey, Matt! I see you!"

I ran. At first, I didn't have any idea where to go, I just wanted to put some distance between me and the oncoming freight train. I was fast, but Tom seemed to be gaining on me. The playground equipment was right in front of me, so I ran up one of the slides, hoping that would slow him down. This was a complete breach of playground protocol, but I didn't care. Tom tried to follow, but he kept slipping. My plan was working!

I ran across the bouncing bridge past two kids who were trying to see how wavy they could make it. I looked over my shoulder and saw Tom reach the top of the slide and head across the bridge, shoving the two kids as he went. I slid down another slide and made a beeline for the Castle, a large wooden structure made to look like a castle with lots of rooms, ramps, and slides. And more importantly, plenty of places to throw Tom off my trail.

I hopped up the wooden stairs and turned to see Tom just starting to go down the slide. I paused for a moment, catching my breath. By this point, most of the kids at school were watching the chase, cheering my escapes. Just before Tom got off the slide, I dove deeper into the Castle, making my way up to one of the windows in a tower. Suddenly, I had an idea. I didn't need to get too far ahead of him, I just needed to stay far enough ahead so he could not catch me but would still think he had a chance at clobbering me.

Looking down from the window, I could see Tom approaching the Castle, but looking around as if trying to decide which direction to go once he entered.

"Miss me?" I shouted down from above. The kids on the playground laughed and cheered. Tom's face grew red as he dashed up the stairs, his breath coming in great puffs of air.

Instead of running back inside the tower, I crept out the window and onto the roof, where I knew Tom couldn't see me from below. I paused, taking a few slow breaths, then began walking along the edge of the roof, backtracking to where I first entered the Castle. I could hear Tom thumping up the stairs in the tower, trying to find me. I slipped off the roof, down the backside of the Castle out of sight from Tom, then ducked under the Castle itself.

"Where's Matt?" Tom bellowed from the tower. The kids on the playground laughed in response to his confusion. Tom looked all around and out the window but couldn't see me. I belly-crawled out from under the Castle and climbed up the backside of the tower, re-entering through the window I had climbed out of, much to the delight of the other students.

"Are you lost?" I shouted at Tom, who was just leaving the Castle.

He turned towards me and was about to shout, but his retort was interrupted by the whistles of the teachers on playground duty. It was time to get back to class. I had survived my first recess.

Kotter and a few other boys were waiting for me as I left the Castle to go line up before we returned to class.

"Matt, that was awesome!"

"You sure showed him!"

"How did you do that?"

The boys were firing off all these questions to me as they patted me on the back, and ceremoniously led me to our classroom's line. And that's when Tom showed up. Everyone went silent. He stared at me, and I wasn't sure what was about to happen. Was he going to smash me?

"Well played," Tom said, giving me a fist bump.

CHAPTER 18

The kids at school were still talking about the playground chase as we left at the end of the school day. My mom walks to the school to pick me up a lot, and today she was in her usual spot waiting for Rachel and me to walk outside. Will was at the nearby middle school now and wouldn't get out for another hour.

"How was school?" Mom asked us as we came outside.

"Everyone is talking about Matt!" Rachel blurted out. Why did she have to open her mouth? I wanted to tell Mom all about it, but not right away.

"What happened, Matt?" Mom asked.

"Nothing big," I said, trying to deflect.

"Whatever," said Rachel. "He outran this big kid named Tom and had everyone cheering for him!"

"What?" Mom asked.

We were leaving the school grounds now and turning south on Nathan Road as we walked

95

home. I guess this was as good a time as any to spill my guts.

"OK, so there's this kid named Tom," I began.

"That's the big kid!" Rachel interjected.

"Let Matt tell the story," Mom gently chided.

"Well, every day we play tag at recess. When Tom is 'it' he likes to shove people hard when he tags them. He likes to laugh when he makes people eat dirt."

Mom started to get a little worked up. My dad always said that's because she is a redhead. Before she could say anything, I kept going.

"Well, he saw me and wanted to tag me."

"Wait, he wants to shove a kid who had a brain tumor?" my mom asked. Her voice rose a little, which is usually what happens before she starts making someone's life difficult. She can be a real momma bear that way, which is usually a good thing, unless I am the one she is getting after.

"Hold on, let me finish," I said, smiling a little. Rachel giggled too.

"So Tom started chasing me, and I ducked into the Castle, you know the big wooden thing on the playground?" I asked.

"Yeah, yeah," my mom replied, wanting me to continue.

"So he followed me in, but I climbed up on the roof of the tower where he couldn't see me. Then I doubled back to where I entered the Castle and yelled at him."

"Yeah, he said 'Are you lost?' and all the kids laughed!" Rachel interjected. Little sisters can be like that sometimes.

"Well, what happened next?" Mom asked.

"The duties blew the whistle, and we all came inside. But," I paused for some dramatic effect, "all the kids were talking about it, and then Tom came to me and said 'well played' and gave me a fist bump."

"Really?" my mom said.

"Yeah, crazy, huh?" I said.

Mom was quiet for a few minutes as we walked down the street. Owen was making goofy noises in his stroller, trying to keep himself entertained.

"Matt," my mom began, "you have been given an amazing gift. Not only have you survived a brain tumor, but you are showing other people that something that horrible doesn't have to define them in a negative way."

"What do you mean," I asked. I was a little confused by what she meant.

"What I mean is that you can show others there is hope after something terrible happens.

Think of it this way. You remember seeing some of the kids in the hospital that couldn't walk or see, or even speak, right?"

"Yeah."

"You have the chance to show other kids that even after a brain tumor, it is possible to have life return back to normal. You'll always have your scars, but you will always be you. Your example can give people hope, and even if their life cannot return to normal because their tumor was a lot worse, sometimes people just need a little extra hope to get them through the hard times."

CHAPTER 19

The December air in Utah felt crisp as we left the hospital. I had my six-month MRI, and Doctor Rockhouse said it looked pretty good. There were a couple of spots they were watching, but because they had not grown, he was pretty sure it was just scar tissue. I could wait another six months before I had to come back. My dad was the only one with me today because Mom had to stay back and help Will, Rachel, and Owen. Dad seemed pretty tense when we left this morning and drove all the way down. I was able to sleep during some of it, but now that we are outside, he seemed happier, almost lighter, if that is a thing. After a lunch at In-N-Out Burger, we continued the drive home. I sat in the passenger seat and started to play a video game on Dad's phone.

"So, Matt," Dad began as he passed a semi hauling a trailer of produce, "I hear you have a unique way of playing playground tag."

"I guess so," I replied, still looking at the iPhone's screen.

"Tell me about it."

I guess Dad wanted to chat, so I put the phone down and looked over at him.

"Seriously, I want to know. Mom told me a little bit, and I thought it was really creative and amazing."

So I shared the whole story with him. He stared at the road, smiling every once in a while. When I was finished, he opened his mouth to say something, then paused briefly before he spoke.

"That's good. I think you will learn that this brain tumor you had—what do you call it again, Pilo?"

"Yeah."

"Pilo—I think you will see that you will be able to help a lot of other kids and families."

I shrugged and looked out at the passing pastures. Utah had a lot of cows.

"Seriously," said my dad. "Surviving brain surgery is a big deal. It's like the doctor said; you are one in a million."

"Maybe. I just want to be me."

"That's just the thing, Matt. This is part of who you are, and that is wonderful. Not many kids can say they beat a brain tumor."

My dad paused, his voice had cracked a little, which didn't happen very often. I hope he doesn't start crying. That would be weird because my dad never cries. Besides, what does he know about being me?

"What if I don't want this to be part of me?"

Dad just stared ahead and didn't say anything. For a minute, I thought he hadn't heard me. I almost repeated my question, but he began to speak instead.

"Well, what if this is your superpower?"

"What do you mean?" I asked suspiciously.

"Think about it. You have all the Avengers beat. The Hulk can turn big and green and has super strength, but only because he was radiated. Thor is a Norse god, so to me, that doesn't count as a superpower. Hawkeye is a great archer, but that is a skill, not a superpower. Captain America is only strong because he was genetically engineered by the Army. And Iron Man just has a suit because he is rich. There is nothing uniquely super about any of them. They acquired their strength through some sort of external force or with a lot of practice. But your strength comes from within. Think about it. Most kids with brain tumors have more than one surgery, and many have to go through chemo, radiation, or both."

"But if I have to have radiation, maybe I'll turn out like the Hulk or Captain America."

"Maybe," my dad chuckled. "On the other hand, why go through the trouble when you already have a superpower?"

I smiled at my dad, and he smiled back. That was about the limit of conversation my dad had in him. He doesn't talk much, and neither do I. I picked up the phone and began playing my game again. I never really thought that surviving a brain tumor was like having a superpower. I wonder if that means I need a sidekick now?

CHAPTER 20

"Mom!" I shouted as I ran through the front door. It was now spring, and it had been almost a year since my tumor was removed.

Mom poked her head out of the kitchen with a look of alarm on her face. She started to say something, but I was too excited to wait to tell her all about Grit League.

"Mom, have you ever heard of Grit League?"

Mom's expression changed from alarm to confusion.

"What?"

"Grit League, it's this new obstacle course race for kids where they have to run through mud, climb walls, and carry heavy things."

"So it's like the Spartan Race?"

"Yes! Exactly," I said, glad I didn't have to explain anything else.

"So what about it?" she asked.

"They are starting a league here in Idaho Falls. It starts at the end of April. I really want to do it!"

"How much is it?"

"Here, let me give this to you," I said as I produced the flier jammed in my backpack.

Mom read over it and started nodding her head.

"That sounds neat," she said.

"So, does that mean I can do it?" I asked, breathless for the answer.

"Let me talk to your father first and see what he thinks."

"He'll let me do it," I said confidently. I know my dad, and I just know he will say 'Yes.'

CHAPTER 21

The warm spring sun felt great. It was great to be able to ride my bike, jump on the trampoline, and goof off with my friends. Rachel and I were jumping on the trampoline to give my mom and dad some time to talk. Dad had just returned from Portland, and Mom was going to talk to him about me doing Grit League. I hoped my dad would say 'yes,' but I didn't want to get my hopes too high. Suddenly, I heard the backdoor open.

"Matt, come inside for a minute," my mom yelled.

"Sweet," I said quietly as I climbed out of the trampoline. I didn't even grab my shoes, I just ran across the lawn to the door. I thought Mom was going to say something about that, be she either didn't notice or ignored it.

"So, your dad and I had a chance to talk about Grit League," Mom started.

"Can I do it?" I interrupted. I didn't mean to interrupt, but I was just too excited.

My dad laughed as my mom looked at him. She gave him this look, like they were secretly able to telecommunicate. It's weird how they can do that.

"Yes," my dad said, "you can do Grit League."

"But you have to be careful," my mom said. "If you fall and hurt your head or if something else goes wrong, we will have to pull you out."

I didn't really hear the last thing she said. I was too excited.

"Thank you, thank you, thank you!" I babbled.

"You're welcome," my dad said. "It looks like your first practice is in a couple of weeks."

"Awesome, I'm going to go tell Rachel."

And with that, I exploded into the backyard. I could tell Grit League was going to be epic—I could just feel it.

CHAPTER 22

A few weeks later, I could hardly sleep at night because I was so excited to start Grit League. My mom and I were one of the first people to arrive at the park where the race was going to be held. Grit League is open for any kid eight years old or older, and even though I am ten, I was one of the older kids. Dan, the coach, started us at exactly 4:30 p.m.

"Are you guys excited to start Grit League?" asked Dan. Dan looked to be in his late thirties and wore a black Spartan Race shirt and some gray running pants.

"Yeah," yelled the kids in the group. There were about twenty of us in all, about half boys and half girls.

"That's not very loud. I asked if you were excited to start?" Dan asked, with his voice rising to a loud roar.

"YEAH!" we roared back.

"Perfect. So, here's how it works. In a minute, we're going to walk through the obstacle course, and I'm going to explain all the obstacles. You have twenty-five minutes to run as many laps around the course as you can. After twenty-five minutes, you have five minutes to finish the lap you are on. Each time you cross the finish line, you'll get one of these bracelets."

Dan held up a white rubber bracelet for everyone to see.

"Just put the bracelet on and keep running. You get one point for every bracelet you collect. I'll send out a newsletter after every race with your rankings. After our fourth and final race, I'll give awards out to the first, second, and third-place finishers for boys and girls. Any questions?"

It all made sense to me. None of their other kids raised a hand.

"Good, let's jog the course. But first, who knows what a burpee is?"

No one raised a hand.

"OK, let me show you."

Dan dropped to the ground, touching his chest to the grass, then pushed up, landing on his feet in a crouch, then sprang into the air with his arms outstretched as if he were reaching for a tree branch.

"That is one burpee. Let's do five really quick. And count them out."

We started our burpees, counting as we went. Some kids stopped after two or three. I did all five, and so did a few other kids. As I looked at the other kids, I realized that if I wanted to win the prize in four weeks, these were the kids I needed to beat. Dan hadn't even said what the prize would be, but I just knew I wanted it.

"Good job, guys! Burpees are hard, and we will do them at every practice. OK, let's go!"

Dan began jogging through the starting line and took us through all the obstacles. First, we had to traverse a balance beam, then climb over a wall. Next, we had to crawl under some ropes on our bellies then climb up, and over a cargo net shaped like an inverted V. After the cargo net, we had to weave through some trees then pick up a sandbag, carry it around a cone, then drop it back off where we had first picked it up. At this point, Dan told us to do five armless burpees, which were burpees without the advantage of using our arms. Those were a lot harder to do. Next, we jogged over to the Z wall, which is a wall we had to cross sideways without touching the top of the wall or falling off. There were hand- and footholds we could use, but they were at crazy angles, which made it more difficult. After the Z wall, we had to cross some monkey bars, but some would twist as we grabbed them. Before we got off the monkey bars, we had to ring a bell. After the monkey bars, we had to throw a foam spear at a target and then grab our bracelet before starting the whole course over again. Any time we fell or messed up on an obstacle, we had to do five burpees.

The course seemed easy enough, but I wasn't sure how many laps I could do in twenty-five minutes. I had never really run that long before. I know my mom was thinking about my brain and what would happen if I fell. I felt fine.

"OK, everybody, line up," said Dan, pulling out his cell phone. "I'm going to start the timer in 3, 2, 1, Go!"

We all took off in a mad dash for the balance beams. Some kids fell off right away and had to do burpees. I took my time and made it across. When we came to the wall, it took me a minute to figure out how to get over it, but once I did, I was able to get to the rope crawl quickly. Some kids log rolled underneath the ropes. Others scooted slowly on their bellies. I got down on all fours and ducked my head under each rope, which allowed me to gain some time on the kids in the lead. Getting over the cargo net was a breeze, and I was able to catch up to some of the other kids as we ran through the trees. The sandbags were heavy, but I passed two more boys as I carried mine around the cone. I beat another kid to the Z wall and took my time crossing it, being deliberate with my hand and foot placements. It seemed like a lot of other kids struggled with this obstacle because there were several doing burpees as I passed them heading to the monkey bars. The monkey bars were hard, but I made it across and headed to the spear throw. I missed my target and had to do five burpees. I would have to do better on my next lap.

During my next two laps, I passed more boys and was in third place. As I crossed the finish line, Dan yelled out that we had twelve minutes remaining. I pushed harder and completed two more laps. As I headed to the spear throw, Dan yelled out that we had one minute remaining. If I hit my target, I would be able to do one more lap and possibly pass the kid in first place who just passed the finish line. If I missed, I would likely finish in second place. I took a deep breath and threw the foam spear. It hit the wooden target with a solid *thud,* and I grabbed my bracelet and pushed on for one more lap.

The kid in first place had just reached the wall and was climbing over it. I hurried through the balance beam, breached the wall and flew under the ropes. I quickly climbed the cargo net and rolled down the other side. I grabbed my sandbag a few moments after the other kid started carrying his. The other kid was slowing down. I passed him right before we had to round the cone and then dropped the bag, sprinting for the Z wall, then the monkey bars. Before I started on the monkey bars, I looked back and saw that the other kid had slipped on the Z wall and had to do burpees. I took my time on the monkey bars, made sure my spear throw counted, and then grabbed my last bracelet. I had finished in first place, something I had never done before.

CHAPTER 23

"Sweetheart, you are not going to believe this," Mom nearly shouted into the phone. She had it on speakerphone and was calling my dad to tell him about Grit League. I was sitting in the front seat, sipping a bottle of water, and eating a granola bar, still surprised by my win.

"What am I not going to believe?" my dad said.

"Matt finished in first place at Grit League!"

"Seriously? How did he compare to the other kids in terms of age and size?"

"Not the tallest or the oldest. Probably somewhere in the middle."

"That's amazing," Dad said, sounding kind of shocked. "Our kid, who cried at every soccer game tore it up in the obstacle course?"

"Hey!" I said.

"Sorry, bud. Didn't know I was on speakerphone. But you did do that at every soccer game when you were little."

"I think Matt may have found his sport," said my mom, trying to get us back on topic.

"I think you are right. How do you feel about it, Matt?"

"Good," I said in between sips. Mom and Dad both laughed.

"I'm proud of you, bud," said Dad.

"Thanks," I replied. "When do you get back?"

"Tonight. I'm about ready to head to the airport."

"OK, that's what I thought," said Mom. "Where are you again?"

"Seattle, so it will be a quick flight and then a drive home. I should roll in around 10 tonight."

"Perfect. We are all excited to see you," she said.

They chatted for a few more minutes then hung up. Mom started the drive home and seemed even more excited than me.

"So really, Matt, how did you like Grit League today?" she asked.

"It was good," I said, not really certain why she was asking me again.

"That's awesome that you finished first," my mom said. She obviously wanted to talk about this some more. I wished Rachel or Owen was there because they like to talk, but Will was babysitting them at home.

"Yeah," I said, smiling at my mom. Maybe a smile would be good enough to end the conversation?

"So, what made you really want to pass the last kid?"

Obviously, the smile was not enough.

"I don't know. Dad told me that when he runs races, he likes to pick someone in front of him and run until he passes them, then he picks another person and tries to pass them. That's what I did."

She raised her eyebrows at me. Why was that so shocking?

"That's a good idea. Looks like it worked."

"Yeah. I think I want to keep going with Grit League."

"I really like that idea a lot. So what made you want to win?"

"I don't know. I guess once I saw that I could keep up with the fast kids, it was like some switch flipped in my brain, and I wanted to pass them."

My mom smiled at me.

"I think Grit League is perfect for you."

CHAPTER 24

My dad seemed nervous. He kept checking the settings of his camera and taking pictures of random things. I knew he wanted to make sure his pictures would turn out nice, but I had never seen him mess around with it for this long. We were at my last Grit League race of the season. I had won all of my races except one. And even that one I barely lost. Dan was walking all of us through the course, which was definitely a lot harder than all the other ones he had built before. I felt a flutter of excitement in my stomach. This was going to be epic!

After a final set of burpees in the wet grass, Dan lined us up and began the countdown. My dad positioned himself near the wall and nodded at me. I nodded back and then watched Dan as he began the countdown. In three, two, one…

"Go!" shouted Dan. All of the other kids surged forward, except me. I held back and settled in comfortably in about the tenth place. After crawling through some sand and walking the balance beam, the lead kids began climbing the wall. When it was my turn, I saw the lens of my dad's camera as I jumped over the top and landed comfortably in the grass.

"Keep up the pace, Matt!" my dad encouraged.

By the end of the first lap, I had easily passed a few kids and was now in fifth place with about twenty minutes to go. At this pace, I knew I could complete six or seven laps before time expired. In other races, I had completed ten or eleven laps, but this one was much longer and more difficult.

My dad followed me around the course, offering encouragement, and updating me on my place in the race. With ten minutes remaining, I was in third place. The two boys in front of me began to slow, but every time I approached them, they would speed up and add some distance. I knew they would do that. I figured if I kept getting close to them, eventually, they would wear themselves out.

"Looking good, Matt. You have less than ten minutes to go," my dad said as I passed near him.

I nodded, feeling a surge of energy. "Tell me when I have five minutes to go," I huffed.

Minutes later, I completed my sixth lap as Dan yelled out the five-minute warning.

"Matt, you've got five minutes!" my dad yelled. He wasn't too far away, but I could tell he was getting very excited.

Immediately, I quickened my pace and caught up to the two other boys who had been battling out for first place. When they saw me, they both began running harder. All three of us arrived at the sandbag carry at about the same time. I hoisted my bag and shuffled forward. The other two boys tried to keep pace but couldn't do it. They were running out of steam fast. I rounded the tree at the far end of the sandbag carry and quickly made it to the drop off point where I tossed it to the ground and headed to the rope climb. I was able to climb and ring the bell before the other boys had even dropped their sandbags. I was halfway through my seventh lap when Dan called time. The other two boys had managed to get through the finish line before time was called and would have five minutes to finish their seventh lap, but at this point, they were battling for second and third places. I had won by about half the length of the course.

"Good job, Matt!" Dad shouted as I crossed the finish line. I could hardly speak and could only focus on trying to breathe. Dad grabbed me some water and helped me rehydrate. Eventually, I could actually speak.

"How do you feel?" Dad asked me after I had recovered a little.

"Awful," I panted.

"Good, that means you gave it everything."

I nodded, trying to swallow some more water. Some of the other boys from the race came by and congratulated me with fist bumps. I chatted with a few of the ones I knew better and then sat on a bench in the shade.

My dad was looking over at the finish line where Dan and his wife were tallying up the points for the season.

"I think you won," my dad said quietly.

"Yeah, I think so too," I said. To be honest, I was more concerned about getting water in my body than accepting any award.

After a few more tallies, Dan stepped forward with the results.

"OK, listen up!" he began. "We'll start with the girls. In third place, winning this cool headband, Addison Baker."

The crowd clapped as Addison claimed her prize.

"In second place, winning this water bottle, Alexis Peterson."

The audience clapped as Dan handed Alexis her water bottle.

"And taking first place and winning this month membership to The Edge Climbing Gym, which includes gear rentals, Madison Woods."

Madison was all smiles as she accepted her prize. I looked up at Jason and smiled.

"That would be sweet!" I said.

"Like I said, I think you have a good shot at it," my dad replied as he turned on his camera and adjusted his settings.

"Now for the boys," began Dan. "There were some really competitive boys out there. But this race is about endurance and stamina. Taking third place and winning this headband, Justin Peterson."

Everyone clapped as Justin accepted the headband.

"You must be Alexis's brother?" Dan asked.

"Yep," Justin smiled. "Thanks!"

"Taking second place," began Dan, "Gabe Packer."

Gabe looked a little disappointed as he walked forward, but graciously smiled as he accepted his water bottle. I began to fidget a little. I wasn't looking forward to being the center of attention, even if only for a brief moment.

"And our first-place winner for the boys is," at this moment, Dan paused for dramatic effect, "Matt Hales."

I felt my face turn red as I walked forward and accepted the gift membership to The Edge. My dad managed to take a few pictures of me and Dan.

"Good job, Bud!" my dad said, slapping me playfully on the back. "How does it feel?"

"Good."

That afternoon, my mom came to me with a smile on her face.

"Matt, what would you think about making a t-shirt about your tumor?"

"What do you mean?" I asked as I snacked on some chips.

"I saw this really cool shirt online and thought we could make it together."

"What does it say?" I asked, feeling a little curious.

"Take a look," she said as she showed me her phone. On the screen was a picture of a t-shirt with *I survived a brain tumor, what's your SUPERPOWER?* written across the chest.

"That's cool! I'd love to have that!"

"Do you want to go to the store and pick out a shirt with me?" Mom asked.

"Sure, but can I finish my chips first?"

"Of course! I'll go start the car."

As she left to start up the car, I felt better than I had felt in a long time. My mom is really good about thinking about others, especially us kids. I wiped my hands off, then headed to the car. Since it was just me and Mom on this trip, maybe I could talk her into a candy bar too.

CHAPTER 25

FOUR YEARS LATER

Spring was here again, which meant I had another MRI appointment. The appointments really aren't so bad. Sometimes the drive to Utah can feel long, it is three hours each way after all. But we always stop by In-N-Out Burger on the way home, which is totally worth the drive. It is hard to believe it has been four years since I had brain surgery. Sometimes kids at school ask about my scars, but only if they didn't know me from back then. Most people don't mention it.

My dad and I sat in Dr. Rockhouse's office for about fifteen minutes before he showed up. Well, actually, it was his resident, which showed up first.

"Hi Matt, I'm Doctor Chen, one of Doctor Rockhouse's residents," he smiled as he walked in. These residents always looked very tired, but at least this one is smiling.

"And you must be Matt's dad," he said, smiling at my dad.

"Yes," my dad said quietly. I know he always wanted them to just cut to the chase and give the results first.

"Matt, let's do a quick neuro check. Hold out your hands and close your eyes."

I did as he asked. I also touched my finger to my nose, stood on one foot, and did a bunch of other things the doctors had been asking me to do for the last four years. Just like every other time since my surgery, I passed easily. Doctor Rockhouse entered as the resident finished my neuro check.

"Hi, Matt!" Doctor Rockhouse said, shaking my hand.

"Hi," I replied.

"How are things going these days?"

"Good," I replied, not sure what else to say. Doctor Rockhouse smiled at me, then looked at Doctor Chen. "How was his neuro check?"

"Perfect," Doctor Chen replied.

"Well, Matt. Things look perfect on your MRI."

I heard my dad release a sigh. He must have been holding his breath.

"Nice," I smiled.

"So, Matt, what kinds of things are you into?"

"I like Grit League, which is obstacle course racing," I said.

The doctor raised his eyebrow like he was unsure what I was talking about.

"If you are familiar with Spartan Races, it's kind of like a kid version of those," my dad said.

"Oh, wow," Doctor Rockhouse replied. "That's some pretty cool stuff." He jotted down a brief note.

"Well, any questions or concerns? Matt looks great, and I don't think I need to see him for about eighteen months at this point."

"No, no concerns from me," my dad said. I shook my head. I was ready to get a hamburger.

"Excellent, well, keep up the good work, Matt," said Doctor Rockhouse as he shook my hand.

CHAPTER 26

I have been waiting for this day for a long time. Coach Dan and his team had set up a Grit League course in a park near the school, and all the kids from the fourth grade and up were going to the park to race against each other. My mom is one of the volunteers helping run the event, and my dad has his drone out to film the race. Most of the kids in my school who know me know I like to do obstacle course races. I'm getting really excited for July. In two months, my dad is taking Will, Rachel, and me to Utah to compete in a regional Spartan Race. Rachel and I will race in the kids' event, and my dad and Will are going to race in the eight-mile event for adults. If either Rachel or I finish in the top three boys or girls races, we can compete in the international Spartan Kids championship race in Nevada this fall. But for now, I am excited to compete in the school race and get ready for the summer Grit League, which starts in a few weeks.

Dan gave his usual speech about the obstacles. We jogged through the course, and he had me demonstrate armless burpees. After we all did five of those, we continued through the course. I noticed some of the kids from school were watching me as we practiced all the obstacles. I wasn't sure why they kept watching me, but I tried to pretend like I didn't notice.

We finished jogging the course and Dan divided us into several groups. There were so many kids running that he had four groups starting about two minutes apart. I was in the first group and saw Tom standing to my left. Tom and I hadn't been in any class together in years, so we hadn't talked much, and playground tag wasn't really a game anyone played any more.

"Hey, Matt," Tom said, offering a fist bump. I bumped him back.

"How's it going?" I said.

"Just like old times?" he grinned.

"Something like that," I said, smiling back.

"Everyone ready?" Dan yelled. We all yelled back.

"Go!" shouted Dan.

The mob of kids pushed forward. Tom elbowed his way past some kids and crawled under the ropes on his belly. I held back a little, letting the other kids tire out on the obstacles.

This course was a lot easier than the ones Dan usually makes for those of us in the competitive league. I cruised through the first few obstacles and hopped the eight-foot wall with ease. The Z wall gave some kids a lot of trouble, but I was able to traverse it without any issue. The lead group of boys were carrying sandbags as I crossed the balance beam. Within seconds, I was at the sandbag obstacle as the lead group was placing their bags on the ground.

Next, we had to run and weave through some trees and make our way to the cargo net. I arrived at the cargo net at the same time as the lead group. Some kids struggled as their feet slipped off the webbing, and they got tangled up. When I arrived at the top, I somersaulted over to the other side and slid down, passing several kids in the process. By now, I was in fifth place, which was where I wanted to be. After the cargo net, we had to cross the monkey bars and ring the bell at the end without touching the ground. The first two bars were stable. The third bar rotated a little, and then we had to grab a softball-sized ball and use that to swing over and ring the bell. The first and second place kids were able to get across, though it definitely slowed them down. Tom, who was in third place, grabbed the rotating bar and fell.

"Five burpees," said Mr. Henderson who was monitoring the obstacle.

"What? No fair, the bar turned!" bellowed Tom.

"It's supposed to," said Mr. Henderson flatly.

When it was my turn, I crossed the monkey bars easily and then hit my target at the javelin throw. I crossed the finish line in third place. Only four minutes had passed, so I still had 21 minutes to go before Dan blew the whistle giving everyone five minutes to complete their lap. I caught up to the other two kids quickly and kept pace with them for the next lap. Tom struggled to catch us, but after slipping on the Z wall, he began falling further behind.

On my fourth lap, I began pushing harder and passed the other two kids. I extended my lead and began lapping more kids. There was still a lot of time left in the race, so I settled into a sustainable rhythm. After the full twenty-five minutes were over, I had finished with eleven laps completed. The second-place finisher had nine laps, while the third-place finisher had completed eight.

Mr. Henderson gathered all of us and explained that the top three finishers would all receive a king-size candy bar, but they would not say who took first place.

"Lame," I heard my dad mutter to my mom. Mom nodded her head in agreement. My dad always felt that people who excel in what they do should be recognized since that is what happens in the real world.

When Mr. Henderson called my name, I walked forward, and Dan gave me the candy bar, a king-size Snickers. All of the kids cheered for me and the other top finishers. It felt good to win.

CHAPTER 27

Utah can be super hot in July. My dad had taken Will, Rachel, and me down here to the "city" of Eden, where we were all going to be running in a Spartan Race. Rachel and I were in the Spartan Kids Race. Rachel had also been running in Grit League and been doing very well. It was fun to watch her pass all the other girls her age and see her either win or come in second place. Here in Utah, if either of us finished in the top three for boys or girls in our age group, we would be invited to race in the first-ever Spartan Kids World Championship in Nevada this fall. My dad and Will were running their first-ever Spartan Race, which was the Spartan Super. Unlike my race, which would only be two miles long, their race would be about eight miles long, going up and down the mountain a few times while going over all the obstacles. I could tell my dad was nervous because he was over-stretching out in the shade, even though his race wouldn't start for several more hours.

I was wandering around the starting line, sizing up my competition. As a family, we had walked around the course as much as we could, which gave Rachel and me a good idea of what to expect. The course was about a mile long, and we would need to complete two laps. In total, we would have to complete nearly thirty obstacles.

"How do you feel?" Dad asked me.

"Good."

"Are you nervous at all?"

"Maybe a little," I replied.

"You'll do great. Just keep in mind that this race is a lot like all the other races you have done. Keep a strong pace and never lose sight of whoever is in first place."

I nodded.

"And don't look behind you. Always look forward." My dad kept getting on me about looking back. He said I had developed a habit of looking over my shoulder, which he said tended to slow me down.

Dad patted me on the back and walked over to a spot where he could photograph the start of the race. The race coordinator called the boys to the starting line and began getting us pumped up for the event.

"Are you ready?" the coordinator yelled.

"Yeah!" we yelled.

"That sounded terrible! I said, are you READY!!!"

"YEAH!!!!" we roared in response.

"On my mark! In 3, 2, 1 Go!"

And with that, we bolted to the first obstacle, a 6-foot wall. I easily scaled the wall and was greeted by a cloud of dust. The course weaved in and out of trees, up and around hills, and down into ravines which crisscrossed the mountainside. I couldn't see my dad, Will or Rachel, but I couldn't think about them at this time. I started the race faster than I wanted to, but I didn't want to let the boys in the front out of my sight.

The rope climb was in front of me, so I leapt as high as I could, grabbed the rope, and climbed to the top using the J-hook method. Once I rang the bell, I slid down and continued along the course into a shaded area where I had to haul some sandbags.

The course eventually wound around the shaded area and then out on top of an exposed ridge. The early morning sun felt hot on my neck. I felt bad for my dad and Will, who had to run at 12:30 in the afternoon. They were going to roast! From what I could tell, I was in third place. The two boys who I thought were in the lead had a pretty long lead ahead of me. I wasn't too worried about finishing in first place. All I wanted to do was finish in the top three. I scaled another wall then spotted my family in the grass.

"Keep it up, Matt! You're almost done with the first lap!" my dad encouraged. I saw my dad take a few pictures as I somersaulted over a cargo net. I was really starting to feel thirsty at this point.

Next, I scaled the inverted wall, hooked around and crawled under some wires before finding the finish line and getting my hand stamped, showing that I had completed the first lap. I heard my family cheer from another grassy area. I was glad they were trying to see me as much as they could along the course. The guy who stamped my hand said I was in third place. The two boys ahead of me were running strong and would be tough to pass, but no other boy was even close to catching me now. All I had to do was maintain my position, and I would be headed to Nevada in the fall.

The second lap was easier in some ways. I kept my pace steady and tried to keep an eye on the two boys in front of me. This time around, I knew what to expect and knew where I could speed up and where I should slow down. What I didn't want to have happen was a fifteen-burpee penalty for messing up on an obstacle. As I rounded each corner, I could see the trail behind and saw that it was still empty, except for one boy I had just lapped.

The rope climb was next, so I jumped and grabbed the rope and tried to J-hook the rope with my foot, but then my grip slipped! I had too much mud on my hands from an earlier obstacle.

"Fifteen burpees," said the obstacle official.

Crap. Nothing to do now but knock out my burpees.

After finishing my burpees, I breezed through the obstacles as fast as I could. Luckily, I hadn't seen anyone pass me yet, and I thought I was still in third place, but I couldn't be sure. Eventually, I arrived at the cargo net, where my family was waiting.

"Let's go, Matt!" Dad yelled. Hearing my dad's voice gave me a quick burst of energy as I rounded the corner and headed for the inverted wall.

"You've got this Matt!" bellowed Will.

"C'mon, Matt" Rachel encouraged.

I made my way over the inverted wall and slid down the opposite side. Rounding the corner, I dove into the mud and crawled under the wires. I emerged completely caked in mud and scrambled down the ravine and then up the opposite side, finishing in third place.

My family caught up to me while I was chugging a sports drink and trying to catch my breath. A volunteer at the finish line was giving me my medal and asking me for my mom's contact information so he could send her the details about the race in Nevada.

"Good job, Matt!" congratulated my dad. "How do you feel?"

"Awful," I choked out.

"I would be worried if you didn't," replied my dad. "So does this mean he has qualified to go to Nevada?" my dad asked the volunteer.

"Yep, I just jotted down the email and phone number he gave me," replied the volunteer. He read the information back to my dad to confirm they were right.

"Yeah, that's my wife's info, so that should be good."

"Good luck in Nevada," the volunteer told me, handing me a banana. "We'll do our awards ceremony at about eleven."

As I walked out of the finish line area, my dad asked me why I had fallen so far behind the other two boys.

"Well, there was this rope I needed to climb, and I kept slipping. So since I couldn't climb it because my hands were too muddy, I had to do a bunch of burpees."

"And you still managed to take third place. That is incredible," replied my dad.

I nodded and drank some more sports drink. I think I would need at least three more of these to feel normal again.

"I think at this point, I just want to take a nap in the shade," I said.

"Deal," my dad said as he turned us all towards a shady spot in the grass.

CHAPTER 28

SPARTAN KIDS
WORLD CHAMPIONSHIP

"Go!" shouted the official at the starting line. As a unified body, all fifty of us boys thrust forward down the trail. I knew I could not hold back at any point along the race. I had to be pushing 110% at all times if I had any shot of winning. Just like my race in Utah, I would have to run two laps around this course, only each lap was about 1.5 miles long instead of only one mile. So by the end of the race, I would have completed three miles of trail running at top speed.

"Go, Matt!"

I vaguely heard my mom yelling above the push of the crowd. I couldn't think of my mom or anyone else at the moment. The only thing in the world, at this time, was the winding dirt trail and the thirty obstacles between me and a cold sports drink.

Balance beams, a Z-wall, a bucket carry, and an inverted wall all greeted me as I completed the first quarter mile. I ducked under some barbed wire and shimmied through some mud before heading to an eight-foot wall. I jumped and grabbed the top of the wall and tried to hook my right ankle on its top, but my foot kept slipping. It was too muddy! I tried twice more and then rubbed my hands as dry as I could. I jumped and grabbed the top of the wall and really tried to hook my ankle on the top as best as I could, and my foot held its grip! I leveraged myself over the wall and dashed down the trail. I couldn't afford any more problems like that.

I passed several boys before arriving at the Hercules Hoist, which requires you to lift a heavy sandbag that is attached to a rope over a pulley. I grabbed the rope and sat down, taking the rope with me, which lifted the bag. I reached up on the rope and used my legs to pull the rope down. The sandbag hit the top, and I lowered it down easily. This was an obstacle, which Dan had taught me how to do. It was about 95% technique and 5% strength. I passed several boys who were still trying hard to pull it down or worse, doing burpees.

The course led up a low bluff to a sandbag carry. Eventually, it wound its way down the bluff to some monkey bars followed by a small tube I had to crawl through. When I got out of the tube, I heard my family for the first time.

"Go! Go! Go!" everyone yelled. I looked to my side and saw my mom.

"This is tough," I croaked through my dry and covered in dust lips.

"You've got this, Matt! Keep it up! Just one more lap!" encouraged my mom.

I carried the next set of sandbags with ease and scaled the inverted wall without issue. Moments later, I got my hand stamped and began his second lap with a renewed sense of energy.

I weaved my way through the obstacles, flying through the ones I was more familiar with, like the Z wall, and eventually turned a corner, heading back to the wall, which had given me trouble during my first lap.

I jumped and caught the top of the wall, then hooked my heel over the top, pulling myself over. I had made sure to keep my hands as dry as possible, so this time around the wall felt easier.

I passed more boys along the course, but I had no idea where I placed in the race at the moment. I felt like I was ahead of the main group of boys, but I had no idea who was in the lead. All I knew was that after the Hercules Hoist, the rest of the obstacles were pretty easy.

I got to the Hercules Hoist and easily lifted my sandbag, but then let the rope loose by accident, causing the sandbag to drop straight to the ground.

"Fifteen burpees!" the obstacle official said, pointing at me. "You have to bring it back to the ground under control."

Frustrated, I knocked out my fifteen burpees then headed to the top of the bluff. No one had passed me that I could tell, but it was all literally downhill from here. I powered through the remaining obstacles and emerged from the tunnel to hear my family cheering for me.

"Go, Matt! You got this! Almost there!" they all shouted.

I hoisted my sandbags, carried them, then tossed the sandbags down. Next, I quickly scaled the inverted wall and sprinted to the finish line. My mom ran over and gave me a big hug.

"How are you feeling?" she asked.

I could barely breathe. I raised my hand and bent over to catch my breath. After a few deep breaths, I was able to manage a response.

"Good, and awful," I said. Mom gave me a few minutes to hydrate and eat some fruit. One of the volunteers checked my race band against the parent's band around my mom's wrist.

"Good job!" the volunteer said, patting me on the back. I walked out and gave my mother another big, dusty hug.

"Alright, let me get a few pictures," said my dad. "Put your arm around your mother, knucklehead."

I posed with my mom, both of us smiling at what had just happened. I think she was just happy to see me finish the race. I was happy to have something cold to drink. I could see, though, that my mom was getting emotional. I could tell this race represented something bigger. This race marked the end of a time where our family secretly wondered if the brain tumor would return. Somehow this race also marked the beginning of a time when my family could finally move on.

My dad took a few more pictures of me by myself, one of me standing awkwardly in front of some Spartan signage, and another with me flexing.

"You rest here with Mom. I'll go check out where you finished," said my dad as he jogged over to get my results.

Mom kept looking at me and patting me on the back.

"Mom, I'm OK," I laughed.

"I know. I'm your mother, I'm allowed to take care of my kids!"

Dad returned after a few minutes with a smile on his face.

"Well, Matt. You finished fifteenth. You are ranked fifteenth in the world!"

I smiled and Mom began to cry. Unlike years ago, when she sobbed in the hospital, these were tears of joy and gratitude. She hugged me again and didn't seem to want to let go.

Everything was going to be just fine.

AUTHOR'S NOTE

Matt's story is one of hope and inspiration. To be honest, I struggled with how to share this experience. It is both deeply personal and, at times, difficult to talk about. However, as painful as it is to relive this experience, my wife and I both felt Matt's story needed to be shared. The irony of it all is that today, Matt remembers very little of the details of the journey. He remembers the hamburgers and milkshakes but doesn't remember what it was like before his surgery or waking up in the ICU. As he has matured, the severity of what he faced has slowly sunk in.

Today, Matt faces adversity just as you read in this story—with grit and determination. I have seen him deal with more than just a brain tumor. He has dealt with the same issues every other child has faced—good grades and bad ones, friend troubles and illness, fear and faith. I felt compelled to write this story to help other kids believe they, too, can face adversity with grit and determination infused with hope and faith.

My wife and I are very sensitive to the fact that not every child battling a serious illness has the same outcome as Matt. We do not know what it is like to lose a child and pray constantly for the welfare of all our children. Sometimes, despite all the grit and faith a family and a child can muster, they lose that battle, and the sick child passes into eternity. While not everyone may share our belief, we believe that families can be together forever and that death is but a brief, though painful, separation. Over the course of the last year, my wife and I have felt Matt was spared because everyone needs hope, and children especially need to know that there is someone out there who knows what they are feeling and can empathize with them. Matt's story gives hope to all who hear it. Perhaps hope is the greatest superpower of all.

ACKNOWLEDGEMENTS

A week after we returned from the hospital with Matt, I was scheduled to run a half marathon in Rexburg, Idaho. I didn't feel ready and tried to come up with every excuse not to run, but with Jen's encouragement, I ran. During the portions of the race which seemed exceptionally hard, I pictured Matt, who was still at home recuperating. I pushed through the negative thoughts and set a personal record that morning. I share this because throughout this whole process of writing *Pilo*, I have pictured Matt in the hospital and pushed forward with the love and encouragement of my wife. Without Matt's quiet example and Jen's strong encouragement, this story would not have been told.

Along the way, I have benefitted from the feedback and editorial skills of many. Jennifer Rees read an early draft and encouraged me to rethink the structure of the story. Her invaluable insight improved the story's flow and really helped bring out Matt's voice. Jennifer Bisbing's sharp eye caught all my deficiencies with the English language and added the professional polish this story deserved. My parents, Bob and Kathy Hales, provided excellent ideas after reading *Pilo* and suggested additional story elements which they recall from their perspective on these events. My brother Scott, the real writer in the family, offered excellent encouragement, suggestions and thoughts on the writing process to help get this manuscript to the finish line.

Again, I cannot thank my wife, Jen, enough for her contributions to the story. We talked for hours on long walks through the neighborhood about how to tell the story, and even why it should be written. Often, when I felt inadequate to write or unwilling to revisit old memories, she would remind me of why this story needed to be told. In short, she reminded me that others need hope. Each night I pray and thank God for my wife, and for sparing Matt.

Lastly, I want to thank you, the reader, for reading this story. I don't know how this book came into your hands. Perhaps you or someone you know has a child dealing with a serious illness. Or perhaps you are a child currently in the fight, or maybe you are like Matt, a survivor. While I don't know your background or what the future holds for you, I hope this story fills you with hope, and maybe a little grit and determination, to get you through whatever lies ahead. Keep fighting and never give up. There is always hope.

CPSIA information can be obtained
at www.ICGtesting.com
Printed in the USA
LVHW111638310820
664634LV00003B/305